DAILY VOCABULARY PRACTICE

Grade 1

Daily Vocabulary Practice provides an engaging approach to building and reviewing your students' skills in structural vocabulary and academic content-area words. The book includes 36 weeks of daily practice and 9 monthly reviews.

Weekly Skill
Practice one skill each week

Monthly Review
Apply skills learned each month

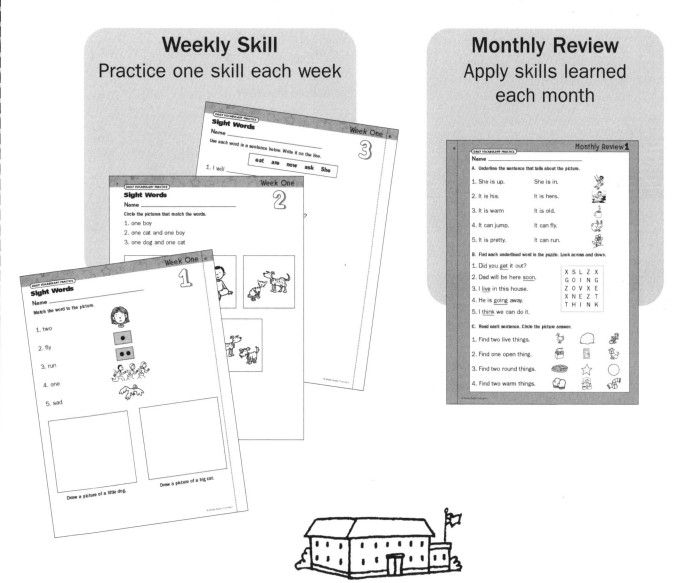

ISBN: 9–780837–481432

1 2 3 4 5 / 10 09 08 07

Table of Contents

Using This Book

Daily Practice

Did you know that vocabulary development is linked to improved reading comprehension and writing skills? In this reproducible book you'll find day-to-day vocabulary practice with essential first-grade words. It's a valuable classroom resource packed with quick and easy-to-use activities designed to strengthen vocabulary and build better readers. You can use these activities in a variety of classroom situations—as everyday warm-ups, quick assessment tools, or helpful reviews.

The book's organization features 36 weekly practice sessions, with three practices in each, followed by a monthly review of words covered in the previous four weeks. This approach allows for in-depth and focused practice of essential vocabulary words in a concentrated time frame. This engaging resource provides high-interest content and vocabulary practice in context.

The exercises offered in the first part of each week are simpler. As the week progresses, the activities are more challenging. Likewise, more challenging vocabulary words are offered as the year progresses.

Later sections of the book feature vocabulary from first-grade content areas including science, mathematics, language arts, and social studies. You might plan to use these sections to complement content-area studies, bearing in mind that through repetition and repeated exposure students' vocabulary grows. It's one more way for students to practice material recently taught and for you to assess students' progress. The book also features a number of sections of vocabulary used in daily life, such as food, clothing, and transportation words.

When planning your daily routine, try one or more of these management techniques:

- Make copies of the vocabulary practice page for students to complete in the morning. Review the activity as a whole group. Review the correct responses together as a large group.

- Distribute copies of each daily page to individual students or to small groups. You might choose to work with students in small groups, or in their reading groups, especially at the beginning of the year. Later, you may want to assign the activities to small groups or pairs of students to work on their own. When students work independently, encourage them to exchange work with a partner and to compare and discuss their answers.

- Use an overhead projector or create transparencies to complete the work in a large group. Ask volunteers to help complete each item. Try completing Day One as a whole-class activity to review the vocabulary words. Then have students work independently or in pairs to complete the following days' work.

- Send the activity pages home for students to complete with a family member. Encourage students to share their work at home.

- Use the materials to complement content area studies. For example, you might have students conclude a lesson on being a good citizen or on geometric shapes by completing the corresponding pages in the practice book.

Monthly Reviews

At the end of each four-week set there is an activity page that reviews words taught during that month. Each monthly review includes simple puzzles and activities to complete.

Extensions & Activities

Helping your students develop and build a strong vocabulary is an ongoing process. This practice book is a terrific tool to help you reach your educational goals. But it's not the only thing you can do every day to help students develop a strong vocabulary.

- Use the vocabulary words in everyday speech. As you use this daily practice book make it a point to use the words in conversation. In this way, you are reinforcing the words, integrating them in a practical way and giving an example of how the words are used in context.

- Read aloud to students. Reading aloud from authentic literature and nonfiction is an essential tool for vocabulary development. By reading aloud, you are introducing students to rich language. You can also reinforce important vocabulary words by engaging students in a book talk, focusing on words you want your students to know.

You can also create additional learning opportunities by incorporating vocabulary words into teacher-created games and activities.

Here are some suggestions:

Word of the Day Choose a word from the week's vocabulary. Challenge students to incorporate the word into their everyday speech. At the end of the day, ask students to give examples of how and when the word was used.

Sight Word Find Pick sight words from the words in month one. Write them on flash cards. As you show each word to the class, challenge students to find it in the classroom—on posters, on signs, on books, on the chalkboard.

Compound Words Write compound words on note cards, then cut the cards in half to form two separate words. Shuffle the cards, then have students put them back together to form compound words.

Super Sentences Challenge students to use the weekly vocabulary words in a sentence. Encourage them to use not just one of the words in each sentence, but several.

I'm thinking of... Play this game. Tell students you are thinking of a word that starts with an S sound, for example. After they have made some suggestions, tell them it has a short A sound after the S. See how many students can suggest words that start with S and have a short A sound. Then add "it ends with a D sound." See how fast students can guess the complete word. Then say, "My new word rhymes with Sad. What could it be?" Take suggestions. Then say, "My word rhymes with sad but it is the opposite of sad. What could it be?" The student who first correctly says "glad" can name the beginning letter of the next challenge word.

Sight Words

Name _____

Match the word to the picture.

1. two

2. fly

3. run

4. one

5. sad

Draw a picture of a little dog.

Draw a picture of a big cat.

Sight Words

Name _____

Circle the pictures that match the words.

1. one boy

2. one cat and one boy

3. one dog and one cat

Sight Words

Name _____

Use each word in a sentence below. Write it on the line.

| eat are now ask She |

1. I will _____ my mother.

2. _____ is a nice girl.

3. We will go _____ .

4. Did you _____ the apple?

5. Where _____ you going?

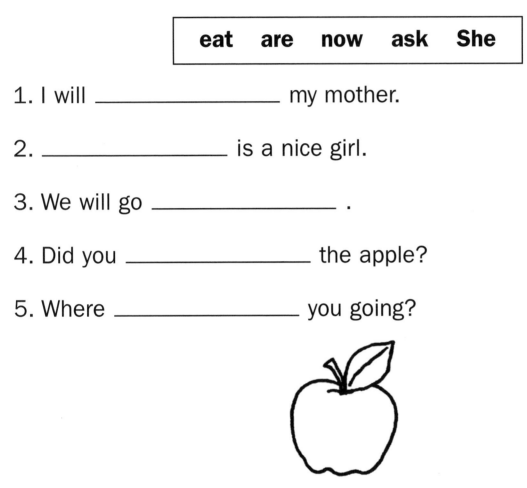

Draw a line from the word to its meaning.

two   not in

new   a number

out   not him

her   not old

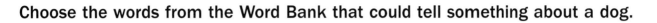

Sight Words

Name _____

1

Choose the words from the Word Bank that could tell something about a dog.

Write one word in each circle.

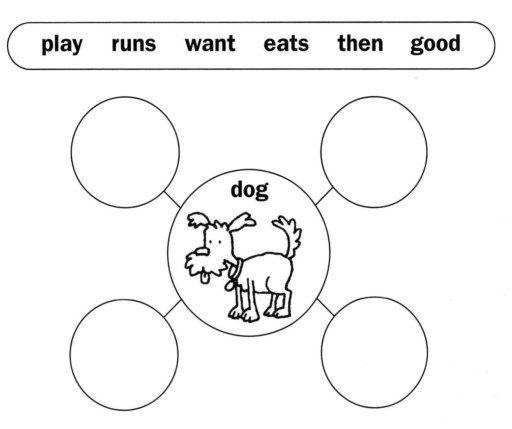

play   runs   want   eats   then   good

dog

Draw a picture of how you play.

Sight Words

Name _____

Choose a word to finish each group of words. Write it on the line.

| ride   come   open   down   home |

1. _____ the slide

2. at my _____

3. _____ a horse

4. _____ to me

5. _____ the door

Add each thing to the picture.

1. blue sky

2. warm sun

3. big dog

4. red bird

5. tall tree

DAILY VOCABULARY PRACTICE

Sight Words

Name _____

Which words name a thing you can DO? Write one on each line.

| ride   this   play   find   must   sing   into   jump |

1. _____

2. _____

3. _____

4. _____

5. _____

Draw a line from the word to the picture that tells about it. Then color the picture

1. give   2. ride

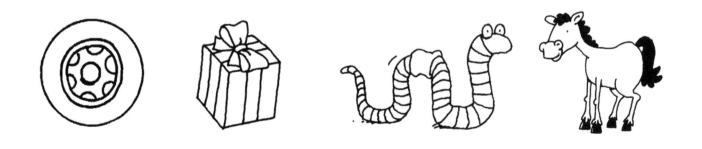

Sight Words

Name _____

| went | make | warm | blue | help |

Use each word in a sentence. Write it on the line.

1. The sun was _____ .

2. Will you _____ me, please?

3. She can _____ a cake.

4. I _____ to school

5. The sky is _____

Make each star the color of the word that is under it.

blue **green** **yellow** **black**

13

Sight Words

Week Three

2

Name _____

Choose the words that could tell you where to look for lost crayons.
Write one word in each space.

over   want   down   soon   under   there

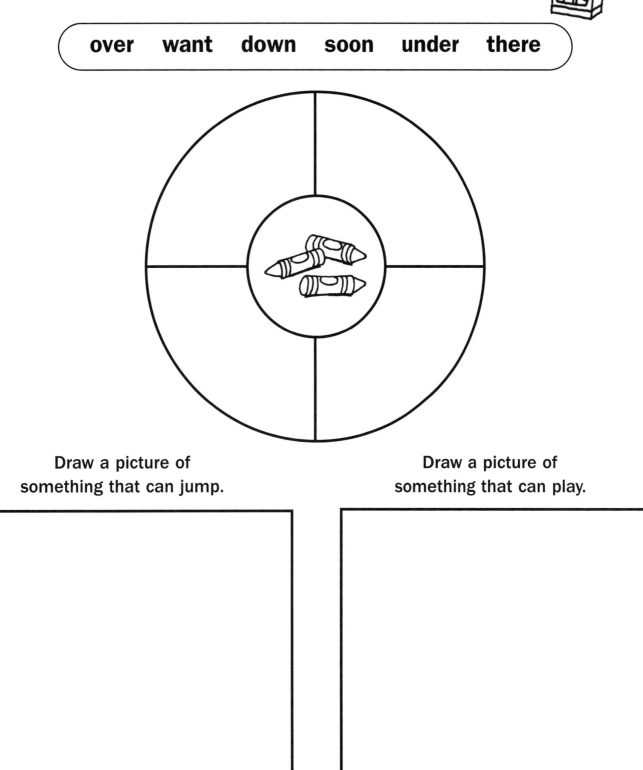

Draw a picture of
something that can jump.

Draw a picture of
something that can play.

DAILY VOCABULARY PRACTICE

Sight Words

Name _____

Choose a word that tells about each picture. Write it on the line.

walk	sing	ride	give	jump

_____

_____

_____

_____

_____

Circle the best picture answer.

1. Which can walk?

2. Which can sing?

3. Which can play?

4. Which can jump?

Sight Words

Name _____

1

Read these words. Write them on a line in the correct box.

> yellow   going   blue   under   brown   there   green

Color Words	Not Color Words
_____	_____
_____	_____
_____	_____
_____	_____

Draw a picture of three yellow things.

Sight Words

Name _____

2

    little   under   down   white   take

Fill in the blanks with words from the bank.

1. Brenda is my _____ sister.

2. She sits _____ the table for fun!

3. We look _____ to see her!

4. I will _____ her out in the snow.

5. The snow is _____ .

Draw a picture of Brenda in the snow.

DAILY VOCABULARY PRACTICE

Sight Words

Name _____

Circle the picture answer for each question.

1. Which is funny?

2. Which is warm?

3. Which has four?

4. Which is round?

5. Which can think?

Read the sentence. Draw a line to the picture that would say it.

1. I can say "please."

2. I am round.

3. I can jump and run.

DAILY VOCABULARY PRACTICE

Name _____

A. Underline the sentence that tells about the picture.

1. She is up.   She is in.

2. It is hers.   It is his.

3. It is warm   It is old.

4. It can fly.   It can jump.

5. It is pretty.   It can run.

B. Find each underlined word in the puzzle. Look across and down.

1. Did you <u>get</u> it out?

2. Dad will be here <u>soon</u>.

3. I <u>live</u> in this house.

4. He is <u>going</u> away.

5. I <u>think</u> we can do it.

X	S	L	Z	X
G	O	I	N	G
Z	O	V	X	E
X	N	E	Z	T
T	H	I	N	K

C. Read each sentence. Circle the picture answer.

1. Find two live things.

2. Find one open thing.

3. Find two round things.

4. Find two warm things.

Rhyming Words

1

Name _____

Rhyming words are words with the same ending sounds.
Long and *song* are rhyming words.

Circle two words in each row that rhyme.

1. man   boy   fan

2. big   pig   dog

3. red   cat   bed

4. pick   sick   sea

5. bark   jay   day

Read the sentence. Circle the rhyming words. Then draw a little picture to show the sentence

My! Look at the beautiful sky.

Rhyming Words

Name _____

Rhyming words are words with the same ending sounds.
Ran and *tan* are rhyming words.

Make five words that belong to the *-an* family.

1. _____ an

2. _____ an

3. _____ an

4. _____ an

5. _____ an

The word van is part of the *-an* family. Draw three things that rhyme with van.

Draw them in the van.

DAILY VOCABULARY PRACTICE

Rhyming Words

Name _____

3

Rhyming words are words with the same ending sounds.
Sat and *that* are rhyming words.

Choose the correct word. Write it on the line.

> mat   rat   hat   cat   bat

1. _____   It says "Me-ow."

2. _____   You play baseball with it.

3. _____   It likes to eat cheese.

4. _____   It goes on your head.

5. _____   It is a small rug.

Use some of the words above to finish this sentence.

A little _____ jumped on a _____

and fell on a _____ .

WELCOME

Long-Vowel Words

Name _____

1

Long vowels can be a, e, i, o, or u. They make the sound of their own names.

Does it have a long vowel sound? Circle yes or no.

1. place	**yes**	**no**	6. if	**yes**	no
2. bone	**yes**	**no**	7. home	**yes**	no
3. mix	**yes**	**no**	8. cake	**yes**	no
4. line	**yes**	**no**	9. use	**yes**	no
5. bee	**yes**	**no**	10. car	**yes**	no

Each word is missing its first letter.

Finish each word. Then write each first letter on the blanks below.

What color word does it spell?

_____ee   This insect goes "Buzz."

_____ion   an animal that is the "King of the Jungle"

_____s   it means you and me; rhymes with *bus*

_____at   what we do with food

_____ _____ _____ _____

Long-Vowel Words

Name _____

Circle the word that has the same "o" sound you hear in *show*.

1. just   cake   go

2. ten   own   game

3. nose   school   sad

4. try   run   open

5. hold   table   bark

Use these words to make silly sentences.

Write the sentences on the line.

ate   Kate   plates

_____   _____   _____ .

snakes   shakes   Jake

_____   _____   _____ .

Long-Vowel Words

Name _____

Finish each sentence with a word from the word bank.
Each has a long "i" sound.

bike	nice	Hide	line	tire

1. Jon is a _____ boy.

2. She rides her _____ .

3. Let's play "_____ and Seek."

4. Please stand in _____ .

5. The car had a flat _____ .

Write an i on each line to make a word with a long "i" sound. Read the word.

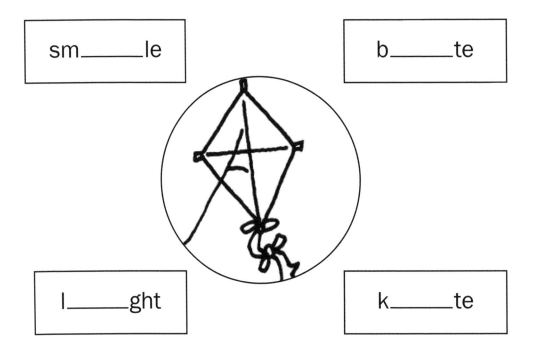

sm____le

b____te

l____ght

k____te

Short-Vowel Words

Name _____

Some words have short "a" sounds. You hear a short –a in *tap* and *pan*.

Circle the words that have the short -a sound.

1. fat   late   bake

2. name   lap   make

3. play   ran   eat

4. each   hat   snake

5. bat   pail   near

Write these short –a words in ABC order. Then draw a line from the word to its meaning.

tan   hat   map   pad

1. _____   light brown

2. _____   wear it on your head

3. _____   use it to find your way

4. _____   write on it

Short-Vowel Words

Name _____

Some words have a short "e" or "i" sound. You hear a short –e in *get*. You can hear a short –i in *sit*.

Use the short-vowel word to finish each sentence.

1. Tim wants a _____ bike.   white   big

2. Where is my _____?   kitten   keep

3. I _____ I could sing.   wish   while

4. My _____ is a dog.   pet   beet

5. Do not get your feet _____.   wet   street

Find these words in this puzzle and circle them. Go across or down.

ship   pan   wet   win   hit

```
S  H  I  P  X
X  Z  X  A  Z
W  H  Z  N  X
E  I  X  Z  Z
T  T  W  I  N
```

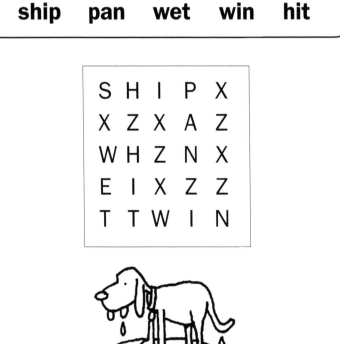

DAILY VOCABULARY PRACTICE

Short-Vowel Words

Name _____

Some words have a short "o" sound or a short "u" sound.
You hear a short –o in *hop*. You hear a short –u in *run*.

Read each sentence. Circle the short-vowel word.

1. She hops to the line.

2. Mary cut the fruit.

3. Mom made a pie.

4. Use a mop to clean the floor.

5. It was a small duck.

A truck has a short "u" sound. Think of something else that has a short "u" sound.

Draw its picture here.

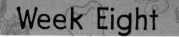

Double-Vowel Words

Name _____

The letters a, e, i, o, u are vowels. Some words have two vowels next to each other.

Circle the double-vowel word.

1. got	jet	need
2. pick	food	work
3. sleep	bus	mix
4. any	line	seed
5. tub	school	father

Draw a line to match the word to the picture.

1. bee

2. feet

3. wood

Double-Vowel Words

Name _____

The letters a, e, i, o, u are vowels. Some words have two vowels next to each other.

Read each word. If it names a living thing, write it under the word "Living." If it does not, write it under "Nonliving."

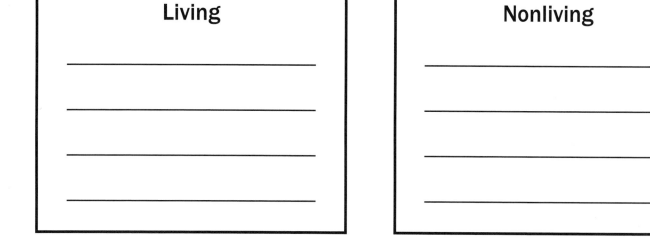

| sheep | tree | book | cheese | floor | room | weed | bee |

Living	Nonliving
_____	_____
_____	_____
_____	_____
_____	_____

Draw a picture of

1. a moon on a spoon

2. a three in a tree

Double-Vowel Words

Name _____

The letters a, e, i, o, u are vowels. Some words have two vowels next to each other.

Finish each sentence. Write a word from the Word Bank on the line.

food	see	tooth	cook	green

1. I used the _____ paint.

2. My _____ hurts a lot.

3. Do you know how to _____ ?

4. Tim eats a lot of _____ .

5. Do you _____ how to do it?

Write –oo on each line then draw a picture of what it names.

1. sp_____n	2. t_____th
3. d_____r	4. f_____t

Name _____

A. Find the rhyming words in each sentence.

1. I will meet you on the street.

2. We can run in the sun.

3. Stand on the side where the path is wide.

4. Lots of dogs bark when they are in the park.

5. The boat will not float.

B. Circle the word that has the "e" sound you hear in *pet.*

Which word names an animal? _____

   1. bed   bee   2. hen   he

Naming Words

Name _____

Naming words tell the name of a person, place, or thing.
Draw a line to match the naming word to the picture.

1. mother

2. grandpa

3. father

4. teacher

5. children

Help the kids get home! The right path has words that name people.
Draw a line on the right path.

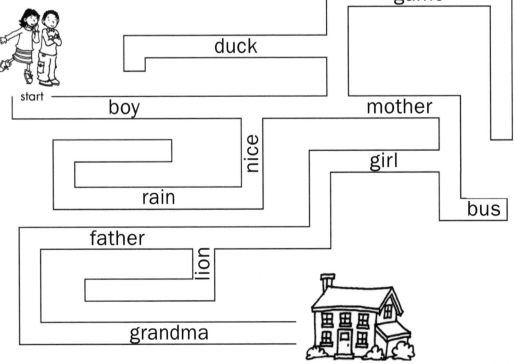

Naming Words

2

Name _____

Naming words tell the name of a person, place, or thing.

Read the words. Write each one in the correct column.

| park   box   zoo   bike   dog   home   ant   school |

Place	Thing
_____	_____
_____	_____
_____	_____
_____	_____

Draw a picture of a make-believe animal. Give it three horns, a yellow nose, and green feet. The rest is up to you!

Naming Words

3

Name _____

Naming words give the name of a person, place, or thing.

Choose the word from the Word Bank and write it on the line.

kite   bed   boat   glass   food

1. You drink from it _____

2. You sleep in this at night _____

3. You eat this _____

4. You fly this _____

5. It goes in water _____

The People We Meet, The Places We Go

Name _____

Peter and *Susan* are names for people. *Smith School* is the name for a place.

Draw a line from a group of words to a matching picture.

1. Circle the place that keeps money.

2. Underline the place to go if you are sick.

3. Put a box around the place you could go for dinner

4. Put a check mark next to a school.

5. Put a red dot on the place you would have a car fixed.

Draw a picture of a special place you know. Write its name.

DAILY VOCABULARY PRACTICE

The People We Meet,
The Places We Go

Name _____

Find the special name in each sentence. Underline it.

1. Tom Jones was in school today.

2. Mr. Platt works at the bank.

3. Sara Bert is my math partner.

4. Mrs. Harris is my teacher.

5. Jon Ross has a garage.

The name of a special person, place, or thing starts with a capital letter.
A period goes after Mr., Mrs., or Dr. Fix these special names.

1. jane moody _____

2. dr fred ryan _____

3. long lane school _____

DAILY VOCABULARY PRACTICE

The People We Meet,
The Places We Go

3

Name _____

Find the special name in each sentence.
Write it correctly on the line.

1. mrs miller got a surprise.

_____

2. She went to apple hill school.

_____

3. At the school, she talked to principal white.

_____

4. He said her son jon miller won the school spelling bee!

_____

5. Jon won a trip to visit the royal candy factory.

_____

Action Words

Name _____

Action words tell about moving, thinking, or doing something. *Run* is an action word.

If the action word tells about moving your body, write it under Let's Move! If it does not, write it under Don't Move.

1

run   paper   hop   very   king   toy   walk   swim

Let's Move!	Don't Move
_____	_____
_____	_____
_____	_____
_____	_____

Draw a picture of two things that swim.

DAILY VOCABULARY PRACTICE

Action Words

Name _____

Action words tell about moving, thinking, or doing something.
Wish is a thinking word.

Write a word to finish each sentence on the line.

1. Sara wanted to _____ about her trip.

   think   **hop**

2. I _____ my friends.

   sleep   **miss**

3. I _____ you come to the party.

   run   **hope**

4. He _____ a new bike.

   swims   **wants**

5. Tom _____ the boy's name.

   moves   **knows**

Write the letter of the picture on the line.

A.    B.    C.

1. Who likes to jump?   _____

2. Who likes to color?   _____

3. Who likes to sing?   _____

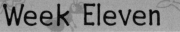

Action Words

Name _____

Action words tell about moving or doing something.

Read each sentence. Circle the picture answer.

1. Which can play?

2. Which can hop?

3. Which can work?

4. Which can cook?

5. Which can bake?

Draw a picture of someone laughing. Show what is making him or her laugh.

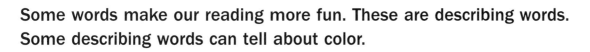

Describing Words

Name _____

1

Some words make our reading more fun. These are describing words. Some describing words can tell about color.

Choose a color word from the Word Bank that helps describe each word below. Use each word only once.

black	green	yellow	white	red

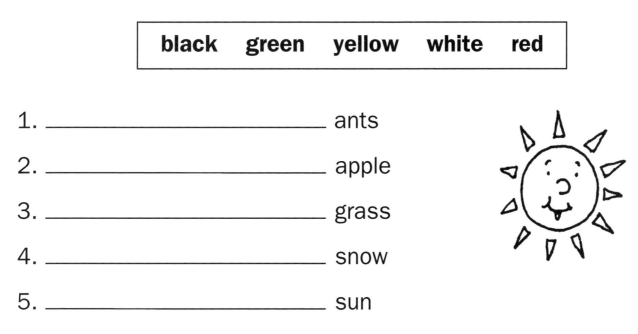

1. _____ ants

2. _____ apple

3. _____ grass

4. _____ snow

5. _____ sun

Choose two things from above and draw a picture of them.

Describing Words

Name _____

Some words make our reading more fun. They are describing words.
Describing words can tell about the size or number of things.

Draw a picture of a thing or things in each part that is big, little, many, or few.

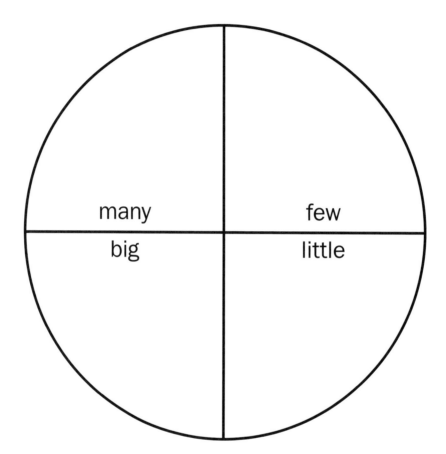

many   few

big   little

Now finish these sentences.

I drew a big _____ .

I drew a few _____ .

DAILY VOCABULARY PRACTICE

Describing Words

3

Name _____

Some words make our reading more fun.
These are describing words.

Draw a line to the matching picture.

1. He was a mean man.

2. Spotty was a silly dog.

3. Jane had a pretty flower.

4. We saw a sad clown.

5. A noisy train came along.

Finish this rhyme. Write a rhyming word on the line.

A noisy train came along,

As we started to sing our _____ .

Name _____

A. Read each word. If it names a person, color the box yellow.
   If it names a place, color it green. If it names a thing, color it red.

1. dad ☐   6. bike ☐

2. boy ☐   7. seed ☐

3. people ☐   8. mom ☐

4. park ☐   9. apple ☐

5. school ☐   10. zoo ☐

B. Answer each question. Write the word on the line.

1. Which green word names where you go to learn?

_____

2. Which yellow word is another name for father?

_____

3. Which red word names a thing you eat?

_____

4. Which green word names where many animals live?

_____

5. Which red word something you ride?

_____

1

DAILY VOCABULARY PRACTICE

Pronouns

Name _____

Circle the best word for each sentence.

1. _____ will use the swing.   I   Me

2. _____ all like to sing.   Us   We

3. _____ are a good player.   You   He

4. _____ have a pretty house.   They   Them

5. _____ will come to my school.   Her   She

Circle the picture that shows the underlined word.

1. We played at Tom's house.

2. He likes to play.

3. She had a lot of fun at Tom's.

4. She gave us cookies.

DAILY VOCABULARY PRACTICE

Pronouns

Name _____

Circle the best word for each sentence.

1. The teacher gave (they, them) the test.

2. The children just looked at (I, me).

3. The children worked on (their, theirs) tests.

4. Jim gave (him, his) test to the teacher first.

5. The teacher took the tests from (we, us).

Read the rhyme. Then answer each question.

The teacher handed out the test
She said, "Do your very best."
"I will try," said each kid
And that is what each kid did!

1. Which words rhyme? _____ and _____

_____ and _____

2. In the rhyme, who is "She"? _____

3. In the rhyme, who are the kids? _____

Pronouns

Name _____

Some words tell you who owns something.
Our, *hers*, *their* and *yours* are some of those words.

Choose the correct word. Write it on the line.

1. The mittens were _____   her   hers

2. The book on the step is _____   yours   your

3. The people stood in _____ places.   their   them

4. We can use _____ ball.   our   ours

5. Did she see _____ mother?   her   hers

Read each set of words. Color the correct word box.

1. belongs to him | her | | his |

2. belongs to them | they | | theirs |

3 belongs to her | him | | hers |

4. belongs to us | she | | ours |

DAILY VOCABULARY PRACTICE

Compound Words

Name _____

Sometimes two words can go together to make a new word. *Butterfly* is made from *butter* and *fly*.

Draw a line from the word to its picture.

1. grand   +   mother

2. grand   +   father

3. air   +   plane

4. break   +   fast

5. birth   +   day

Look at the pictures and say their names. Find that word in the Word Bank. Write it on the line

| blackbird   doghouse   cupcake |

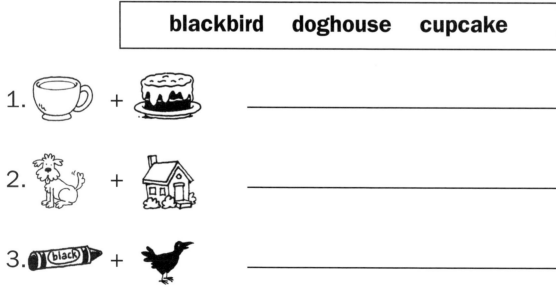

1. _____

2. _____

3. _____

DAILY VOCABULARY PRACTICE

Compound Words

Name _____

Find each picture's name in the Word Bank. Write it on the line.

| fireplace   starfish   baseball   playground   snowflake |

1. _____

2. _____

3. _____

4. _____

5. _____

Follow the directions.

Susie Starfish   **Tommy Starfish**   _____ starfish

1. Color Susie Starfish red.

2. Give Tommy Starfish two eyes and a smile. Color him yellow.

3. Finish the third star's name. Color it whatever you like.

Compound Words

Name _____

Sometimes two words can go together to make a new word.
Something is made from *some* and *thing*.

Choose the correct word from the Word Bank. Write it on the line.

Maybe   without   everywhere   outside   Someone

1. _____ took my book!

2. I cannot read _____ it.

3. Did I leave it _____ ?

4. I have looked _____ .

5. _____ I will find it.

pancake   birthday   outside   homework

Read each word on the goldfish. Follow these directions.

1. Which word names a food? Color the fish blue.

2. Which word names the day you are a year older?
   Color the fish green.

3. Which word names work you do at home?
   Color the fish brown.

4. Which word is the opposite of *inside*? Color the fish orange.

5. Circle all the fish that are going to the right.

DAILY VOCABULARY PRACTICE

Synonyms

Name _____

Sometimes words can have the same meaning.
Look and *see* are words that mean the same.

Draw a line between two words that mean almost the same thing.

1. ant   lady

2. small   kind

3. house   little

4. nice   home

5. woman   bug

Color the space with the word that is does NOT mean earth.

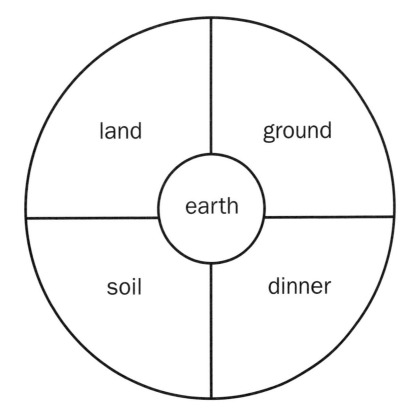

Synonyms

Name _____

Sometimes words can have the same meaning. *Look* and *see* have the same meaning.

Choose a word to finish each sentence from the word bank. The word below the sentence gives you a clue.

> **store   shout   harm   hop   bee**

1. Molly saw a _____ on the cake.
   (bug)

2. Do not _____ my rabbit.
   (hurt)

3. You cannot _____ here.
   (yell)

4. We went into a nice _____ .
   (shop)

5. Can you _____ over the log?
   (jump)

Read each word at the top. Which word below means almost the same thing?

Write it on the line.

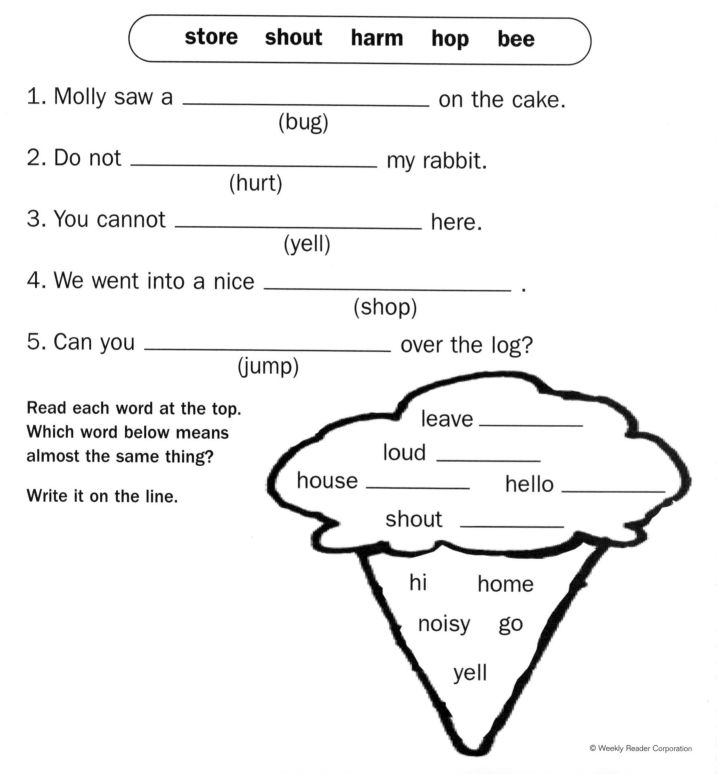

leave _____

loud _____

house _____   hello _____

shout _____

hi   home

noisy   go

yell

DAILY VOCABULARY PRACTICE

Synonyms

Name _____

Sometimes words can have the same meaning. *Look* and *see* are words that have the same meaning.

Read each pair of words. If they mean almost the same thing, color the star yellow. If not, color the star red.

1. choose   pick   ☆

2. shout   yell   ☆

3. sun   tree   ☆

4. feel   touch   ☆

5. build   make   ☆

6. kind   nice   ☆

Think of some words that mean almost the same thing as *kind*.
Write them on the lines below.

_____

_____

_____

_____

Opposites

Name _____

Opposites tell about things that are very different from one another.

Draw a line between opposites.

1.

2.

3.

4.

5.

Draw a picture of something that is big.	Draw a picture of something that is small.

Opposites

2

Name _____

Opposites tell about things that are very different from one another.

Choose a word from the Word Bank to finish each set. Write it on the line.

stop	day	cold	happy	big

1. You are not sad. You are _____ .

2. It is not little. It is _____ .

3. The car could not go. It had to _____ .

4. We sleep at night. We play in the _____ .

5. She was not hot. She was _____ .

Read the word in each raindrop. Find its opposite on the umbrella. Write it on the line.

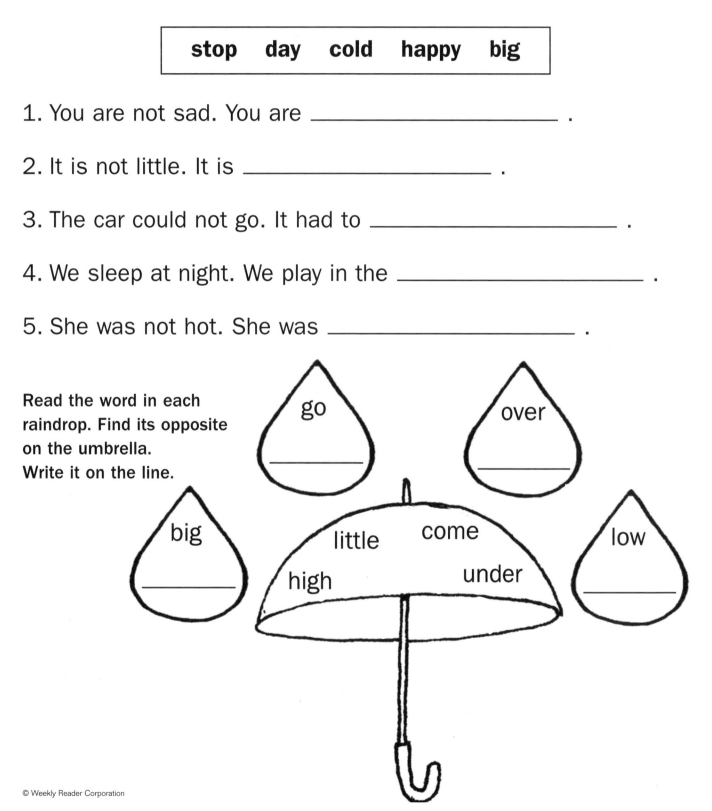

go _____

over _____

big _____

little   come

high   under

low _____

DAILY VOCABULARY PRACTICE

Opposites

Name _____

3

Choose an opposite word from the Word Bank. Write it on the line.

> **always   up   open   runs   new**

1. Josh goes _____ to see his grandmother.
(down)

2. Her door is _____ for him.
(closed)

3. He _____ to her house.
(walks)

4. Josh gets _____ crayons from grandmother.
(old)

5. Josh _____ likes grandmother's house.
(never)

Look in the puzzle. Find an opposite of each of these words. Go across or down.

> **black   dry   laugh   stop**

```
W  H  I  T  E
C  G  O  X  O
R  O  W  E  T
Y  X  O  X  O
```

Name _____

A. Fix each sentence. Cross out the incorrect word.
   Write the correct word on the line.

1. She showed we how to do it. _____

2. Where did you find is?   _____

3. He gave my the picture.   _____

B. Draw a line between the words that are opposites.

1. up   under

2. over   front

3. back   out

4. start   down

5. in   stop

C. Underline the meaning of each word.

1. butterfly   a flower   an insect

2. backpack   a bag   a bed

3. bedroom   place to eat   place to sleep

How We Travel

Name _____

How do people go places? Transportation words tell you.

Draw a line to match each word to a picture.

1. car

2. wagon

3. truck

4. van

5. bus

6. train

Choose one thing from above. Draw a picture with you in it!

DAILY VOCABULARY PRACTICE

How We Travel

Name _____

2

How do people go places? Transportation words tell you.

Look at the word in the top of each box. Color the part in the bottom that shows what the word means.

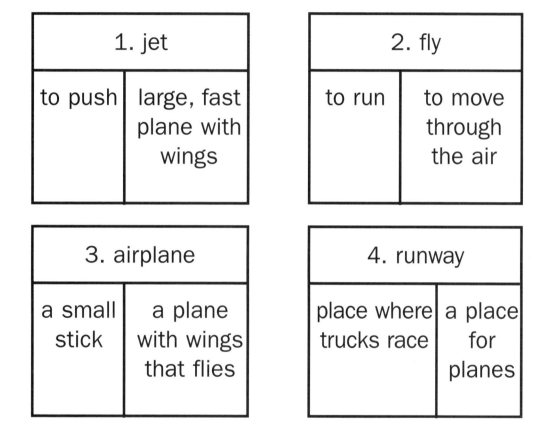

1. jet	
to push	large, fast plane with wings

2. fly	
to run	to move through the air

3. airplane	
a small stick	a plane with wings that flies

4. runway	
place where trucks race	a place for planes

Look at the puzzle. Circle the words from the Word Bank. Look across and down.

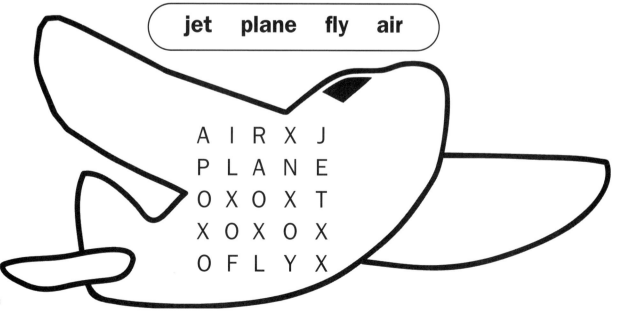

jet   plane   fly   air

```
A I R X J
P L A N E
O X O X T
X O X O X
O F L Y X
```

DAILY VOCABULARY PRACTICE

How We Travel

Name _____

How do people move around? Transportation words tell you.

Find each picture's name. Write its letter on the line.

1. _____   a. canoe

2. _____   b. fishing boat

3. _____   c. submarine

4. _____   d. sailboat

5. _____   e. ocean liner

Put these sentences in order to tell a little story. Number them 1, 2, 3, or 4.

_____ Jon and dad got in the row boat.

_____ Jon and dad rowed around the lake.

_____ Jon and dad put the row boat in the water.

_____ Jon and dad put on life jackets.

What We Eat

Week Eighteen

1

Name _____

Yum! What is your favorite fruit or vegetable?

Look at each circle. Write an e on each line. If the picture matches the word, color it. If it does not, put an X through it.

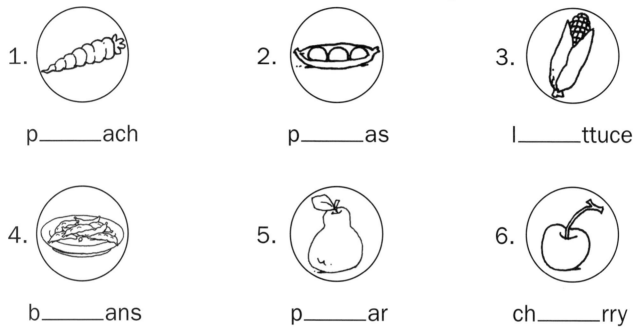

1. p_____ach

2. p_____as

3. l_____ttuce

4. b_____ans

5. p_____ar

6. ch_____rry

Draw a picture of your favorite fruit here.

What We Eat

Name _____

These foods are good to eat!

Draw a line from the picture to the word.

1. fish

2. pasta

3. crackers

4. meat

5. nuts

Which foods have milk in them? Draw a picture to go with each name.

ice cream

cheese

milk

yogurt

hot chocolate

What We Eat

3

Name _____

How do we cook?

> stove   boil   bake   fry   mix

Read the clue. Choose the correct word from the Word Bank. Write the word on the line.

1. We put things together.   _____

2. We cook food in an oven.   _____

3. We cook food in water.   _____

4. We cook food in a low pan on heat.   _____

5. We use this to cook food.   _____

Read the rhyme. Then answer the questions.

Boil, mix, stir, and shake
Cookies take some time to make.

Roll, press, put them in.
Nice warm cookies make us grin!

1. Which words rhyme? _____ and _____

2. _____ and _____

3. Find the word that rhymes with *fix*. Write it here. _____

4. Which thing could you use to *stir*?

What We Wear

Name _____

What do you wear on your feet?

Draw a line from the words to the correct picture.

1. to dress up

2. to run and play

3. in the snow

4. when it is hot

5. in your pajamas

Circle the correct picture to finish the little rhyme.

Here is something that rhymes with *fox*.

They go on your feet. They are _____ .

Week Nineteen

What We Wear

2

Name _____

We wear some clothes in cold weather to keep warm.

Write the correct clothing word on the line.

1. Please wear a warm _____.   cot   coat

2. Your _____ will   maybe   mittens
   keep your hands warm.

3. Put your _____   scarf   school
   around your neck.

4. A _____ keeps   help   hat
   your head warm.

5. Tall _____ keep   books   boots
   the cold from your feet.

Follow each direction below.

1. These keep your feet warm. Color them blue.

2. These keep your hands warm. Color them red.

3. This keeps your head warm. Color it yellow and green.

What We Wear

Name _____

3

Which would you wear in hot weather? Circle the picture answer.

1. To swim, Todd wears
   a _____ .

jacket   swim suit

2. At the playground, Kim
   wears _____ .

shorts   snow pants

3. To go to a friend's house,
   Bill wears _____ .

snow boots   sandals

4. To swim, Jen wears
   a _____ .

dress   swim suit

5. At the beach, Mrs. Jones
   needs _____ .

sun glasses   ski hat

Look at the picture. Unscramble the letters to find its name. Write it on the line.

1. uns   ____ ____ ____

2. tha   ____ ____ ____

3. htsors   ____ ____ ____ ____ ____ ____

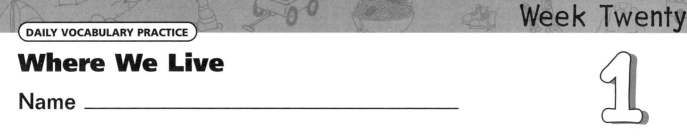

DAILY VOCABULARY PRACTICE

Where We Live

Name _____

1

People live in different kinds of homes.

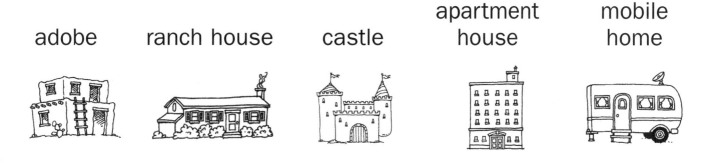

| adobe | ranch house | castle | apartment house | mobile home |

Read the word. Put an X next to what it means.

1. adobe

_____ a house of dry baked mud

_____ a house of snow

2. castle

_____ a home for a king

_____ a small home

3. ranch house

_____ a one-story house

_____ house with no roof

4. apartment

_____ a building with many homes

_____ a tent

5. mobile home

_____ can have wheels and move around

_____ house made of mud

Draw a castle.

Where We Live

Name _____

Animals live in different kinds of homes.

hive   nest   barn   burrow   dog house

Choose a word from the Word Bank. Write it on the line.

1. We saw a bird's _____ in a tree.

2. The groundhog dug its _____ .

3. Honey bees live in a _____ .

4. Spot stays in his _____ .

5. The cows were in the _____ .

Draw a dog house.

1. Color it yellow.

2. Give it a red roof.

3. Put green grass around it.

4. Draw a little hill on the right side.

5. Put a brown dog near the dog house.

6. Put a bone near the dog.

Where We Live

3

Name _____

Some homes are special shapes.

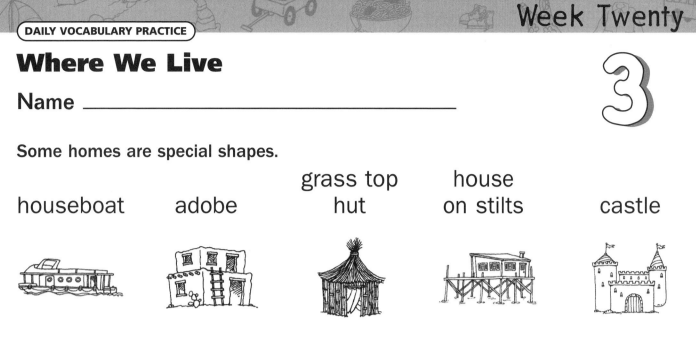

houseboat   adobe   grass top
hut   house
on stilts   castle

Draw a line from the picture to the words that tell about it.

1.    a home for a person who likes to fish

2.    a home with a grass top

3.    a home for a king

4.   a house of baked mud bricks

5.    a house with legs to keep it dry

Finish this sentence by drawing a picture to show what you mean.

Where I live is great because _____ ...

Name _____

A. Read each word. If the word tells about transportation write the word under "Yes." If it does not, write it under "No."

happy	car	sing	boat	sleep	jet
those	ship	pan	road	wagon	nice

Yes	No
_____	_____
_____	_____
_____	_____
_____	_____
_____	_____
_____	_____

B. Write each food word under the correct heading.

cheese	yogurt	corn	carrot	blueberry	orange

Milk Foods	Fruits	Vegetables
_____	_____	_____
_____	_____	_____

How We Find Our Way

Name _____

We have many kinds of land on Earth.

Choose a word to complete each sentence. Write it on the line.

> **all   up   grow   went   hot**

1. We looked _____ at the big mountain.

2. The desert is _____ and dry.

3. The island had water _____ around it.

4. Farmers _____ crops on the plains.

5. Jon _____ up the hill near his house.

Circle four words in the puzzle that rhyme with *hill*. Go across or down.

```
O  X  O  P  F
X  O  X  I  I
W  I  L  L  L
X  S  I  L  L
```

How We Find Our Way

Name _____

We have different kinds of water on Earth.

Read each word. If it names water, write it under "Water."
If it does not, write it under "Not Water."

river	street	ocean	walk	pond	hop	lake	clown

Water	Not Water
_____	_____
_____	_____
_____	_____
_____	_____

What lives in the ocean?
Draw a picture to show it.

What lives in a river?
Draw a picture to show it.

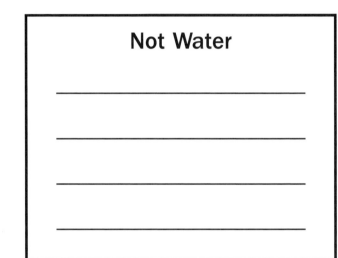

How We Find Our Way

Name _____

Maps and map words help us find our way.

Choose the best word to finish each sentence.

> **shows   near   north   go   us   take**

1. Which road should we _____ ?

2. I think Highway 81 is the way to _____ .

3. What town is that road _____ ?

4. This map will help _____ .

5. It _____ that the road goes south.

6. Which way is _____ ?

Match the picture to the correct word or words.

1   state

2.   map key

3.   globe

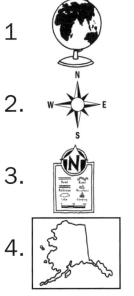

4.   directions

DAILY VOCABULARY PRACTICE

Special Days, Special Times

Name _____

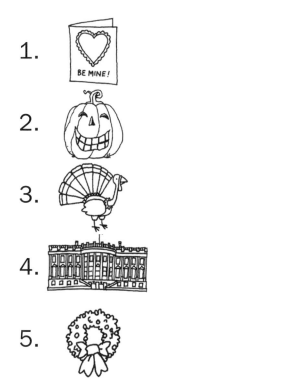

Look at the picture. Which holiday does it stand for?

Draw a line from the picture to the words.

1.   Halloween

2.   Valentine's Day

3.   Christmas

4.   Thanksgiving

5.   Presidents' Day

Follow each step.

1. Give the first pumpkin a smile.

2. Make the third pumpkin look sad.

3. Give the second pumpkin green hair and a mouth.

4. Make the last pumpkin look the way you like.

Special Days, Special Times

Name _____

2

How do we celebrate special days?

Which words name a way people celebrate? Write them under "Let's Celebrate."

sing	mouse	laugh	dance
talk	games	cry	eat	work

Let's Celebrate

_____

_____

_____

_____

_____

_____

Color the picture if it makes you think of a special day.

DAILY VOCABULARY PRACTICE

Special Days, Special Times

Name _____

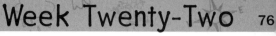

Read the story. Then answer each question.

On **Valentine's Day**, Joe had a party.

Everyone got a Valentine **card** from Joe.

Everyone had **cupcakes** and juice.

It was a fun **time** for **all**.

1. Which dark words name a holiday?

_____

2. Which dark word starts with c and rhymes with *hard*?

_____

3. Which dark word is a compound word?

_____

4. Which dark word starts with t and has a long -i sound?

_____

5. Which dark word rhymes with *tall*?

_____

Now write a sentence using two or three of the dark words.

_____

We Are Good Citizens

Name _____

1

We care about our country.

Draw a line from each word to what it means.

president

White House

capital

country

flag

stars and stripes

leader of our country

United States

our president's home

Washington, D.C.

Draw and color a flag that shows something about you!

DAILY VOCABULARY PRACTICE

We Are Good Citizens

Name _____

We care about others.

Choose the word to finish the sentence. Write it on the line.

> **help   cares   trust   fair   count on**

1. Tom, Can you _____ me put up the flag?

2. We must be _____ when we play this game.

3. I _____ you to tell the truth.

4. Sara _____ for her little sister.

5. Can I _____ _____ you?

Draw a line to match the picture to the sentence.

1. She cares for her child.

2. Jill helps her teacher.

3. Bill says, "Please" when he needs something.

We Are Good Citizens

Name _____

Get through the maze to salute our flag. Find the path through the box that makes a correct sentence.

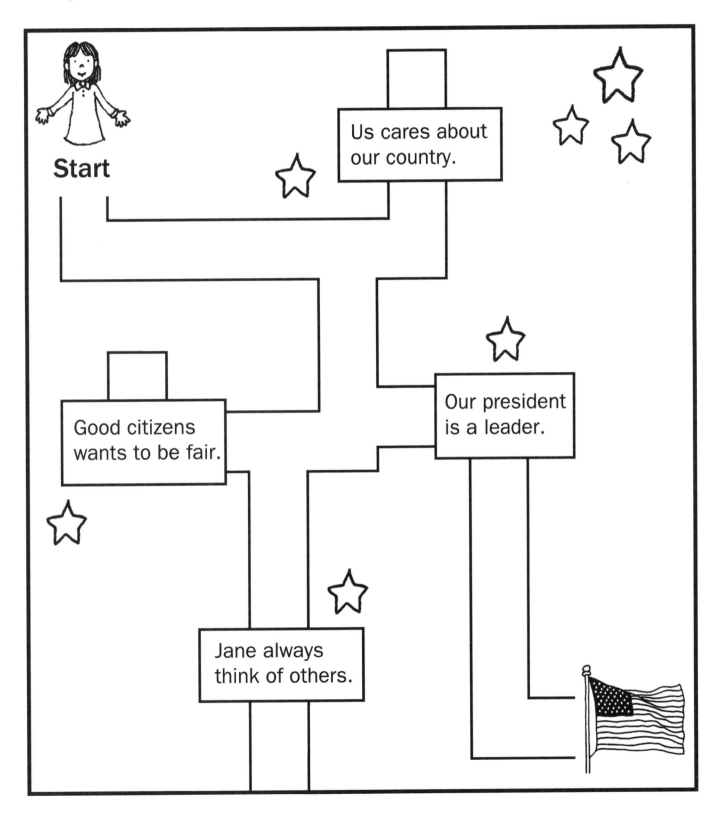

Start

Us cares about our country.

Good citizens wants to be fair.

Our president is a leader.

Jane always think of others.

Our Community

Name _____

Our school is a community.

Write the correct word on the line.

$$\boxed{\text{books} \quad \text{special} \quad \text{lunch} \quad \text{papers} \quad \text{leads}}$$

1. The principal is the person who _____ our school.

2. We eat _____ in our cafeteria.

3. Our pencils and _____ are in our desks.

4. The school library has so many _____ !

5. Our teacher is so _____ .

Write three words that rhyme with lunch.

_____

_____

_____

Our Community

Name _____

Our town is a community.

| town   store   car   family   neighbors |
| table   friends   TV   playground |

Read each word. Then write it under a heading below.

Place	People	Thing
_____	_____	_____
_____	_____	_____
_____	_____	_____

Draw a picture of two things that rhyme with swing.

Our Community

Name _____

A community has helpers. Look at each picture.
Find the name of the helper and write it on the line.

| doctor   mail carrier   baker   firefighter |
| police officer   traffic guard   dentist   nurse |

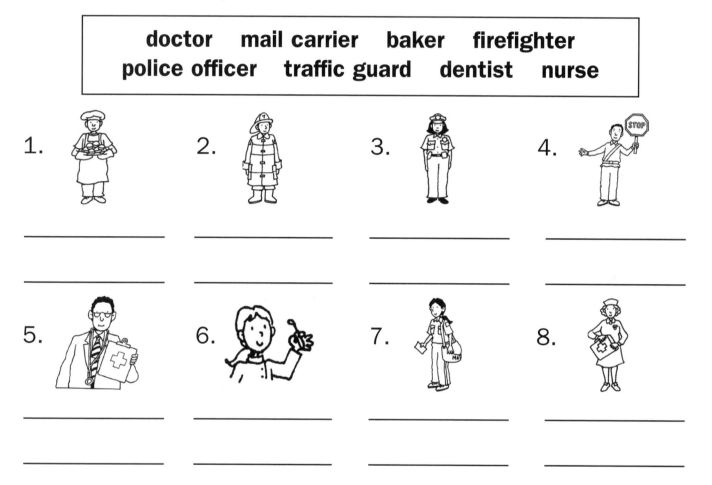

1. _____   2. _____   3. _____   4. _____

5. _____   6. _____   7. _____   8. _____

Help me watch and listen, too
I know that I must look for you.

Near my school you stand
    each day
To make traffic stop and stay.

When I safely cross the street,
Blow your whistle, "tweet,
    tweet, tweet"

1. Which word rhymes with day?

_____

2. Which word names a place
   you go to learn?

_____

3. Which word is a name for
   cars, buses, and trucks?

_____

DAILY VOCABULARY PRACTICE

Name _____

A. Write an –a on each line and read the word. Circle the picture that shows it.

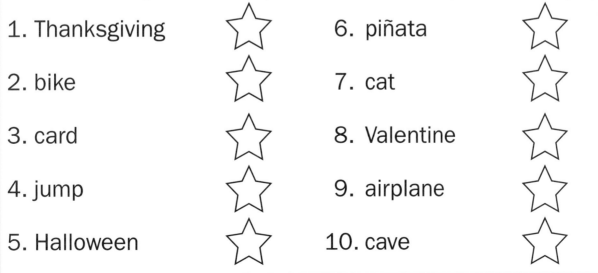

1. m____p

2. l____ke

3. b____ll

4. isl____nd

5. mount____in

6. oce____n

7. ro____d

8. st____te

B. If it is a holiday word or words, color the star red. If not, color the star purple.

1. Thanksgiving ☆

2. bike ☆

3. card ☆

4. jump ☆

5. Halloween ☆

6. piñata ☆

7. cat ☆

8. Valentine ☆

9. airplane ☆

10. cave ☆

Earth, Our Home

Name _____

Many things make up our Earth.

Add an –a to each word. Write the Earth word on the line.

1. l_____nd

_____

2. c_____ve

_____

3. _____ir

_____

4. r_____in

_____

5. be_____ch

_____

6. w_____ter

_____

Circle the second Earth.

Circle the fourth sun.

Circle the third rock.

Earth, Our Home

2

Name _____

Earth changes in many ways.

shakes   harm   blow   fall   sky   trees

Write the correct word on the line.

1. Earth's four seasons are winter, summer, spring,

   and _____.

2. Before winter many _____ lose their leaves.

3. Before a storm we see clouds in the _____ .

4. The wind may _____ too.

5. An earthquake _____ the ground.

6. Earthquakes can _____ homes and cars.

Write two words that rhyme.

sun   air

_____   _____

_____   _____

Earth, Our Home

Name _____

We care for our Earth.

Choose the best word. Write it on the line.

| Turn | Keep | cans | litter | clean |

1. _____ the water off when you brush your teeth.

2. _____ paper bags to use again.

3. Pick _____ up from the ground.

4. Recycle paper, bottles, and _____ .

5. Help make Earth a _____ place.

Follow each direction.

1. It rhymes with *bark* and starts with –*p*.

   Write it here. _____

2. It rhymes with *lock* and starts with –*r*.

   Write it here. _____

3. It rhymes with *cave* and starts with –*s*.

   Write it here. _____

87

Up in Space

Name _____

Draw a line from the picture to the space word.

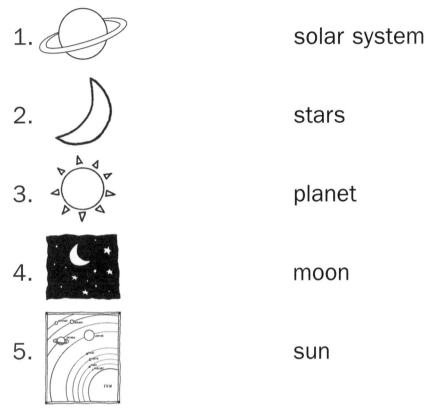

1.   solar system

2.   stars

3.   planet

4.   moon

5.   sun

Color each space picture.

DAILY VOCABULARY PRACTICE

Up in Space

2

Name _____

There are eight planets around our sun. Find each planet. Write its name on the line.

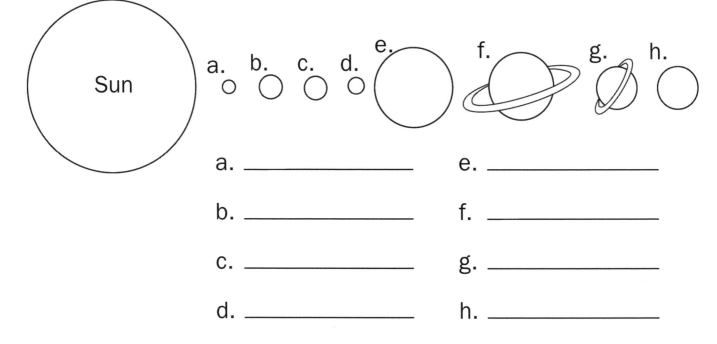

a. _____   e. _____

b. _____   f. _____

c. _____   g. _____

d. _____   h. _____

1. Mercury is the smallest planet.

2. Venus is between Mercury and Earth.

3. Earth is the third planet.

4. Mars comes right after Earth.

5. Jupiter is the biggest planet.

6. Saturn has rings.

7. Uranus comes right after Saturn.

8. Neptune is last.

Now color each planet.

1. Make Mercury green.

2. Make Venus yellow.

3. Color Earth blue and green.

4. Mars is the red planet.

5. Make Jupiter gray and brown.

6. Color Saturn orange with red rings.

7. Uranus can be light blue.

8. Make Neptune dark blue.

Up in Space

3

Name _____

Travel to space!

Write the correct word on the line.

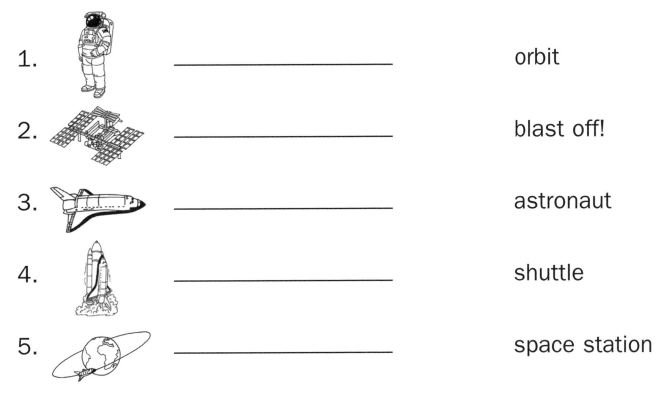

1. _____   orbit

2. _____   blast off!

3. _____   astronaut

4. _____   shuttle

5. _____   space station

Solve the riddle.

Which planet likes to sing?

Write the first letter of each picture name. Then read the answer!

____ ____ ____   ____ ____ ____ ____

(DAILY VOCABULARY PRACTICE)

You and Your Body

Name _____

1

Keep a healthy body.

Draw a line from each picture to the word that names it.

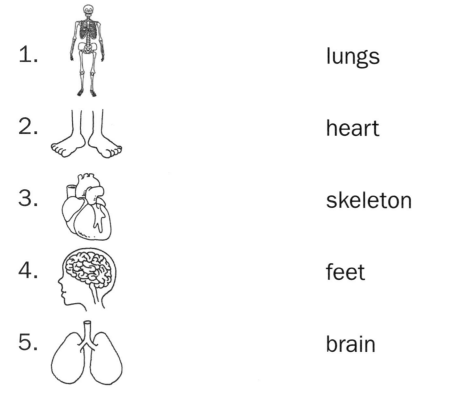

1.   lungs

2.   heart

3.   skeleton

4.   feet

5.   brain

Circle yes if the sentence is true. Circle no if it is not.

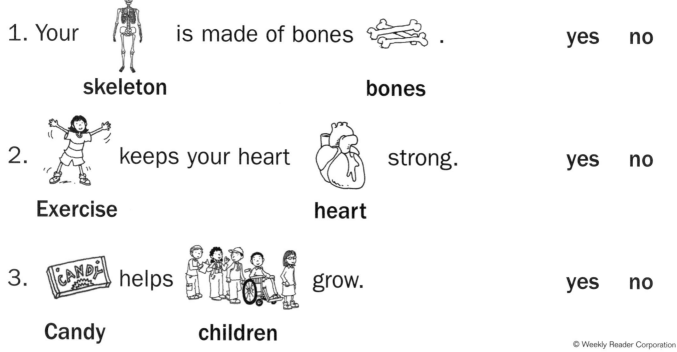

1. Your   is made of bones   .   **yes**   **no**

     skeleton   **bones**

2.   keeps your heart   strong.   **yes**   **no**

  Exercise   **heart**

3.   helps   grow.   **yes**   **no**

  Candy   **children**

DAILY VOCABULARY PRACTICE

You and Your Body

Name _____

We visit the doctor. Circle the word that tells about the picture.

1. doctor   father   nurse

2. cloud   sick   long

3. X-ray   train   small

4. mouse   happy   medicine

5. town   well   stone

a   checkup   Get   year.   every

The Healthy Bears are here

To say, "Be fit and strong."

Visit the doctor, eat good foods,

Keep healthy all year long!

The bears have a message for you. Write one word on each line to read it.

_____ _____ _____ _____ _____ .

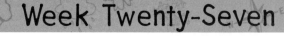

You and Your Body

Name _____

3

We visit the dentist.

Match the word in the first tooth to its meaning in the second tooth.
Write the letter on the line.

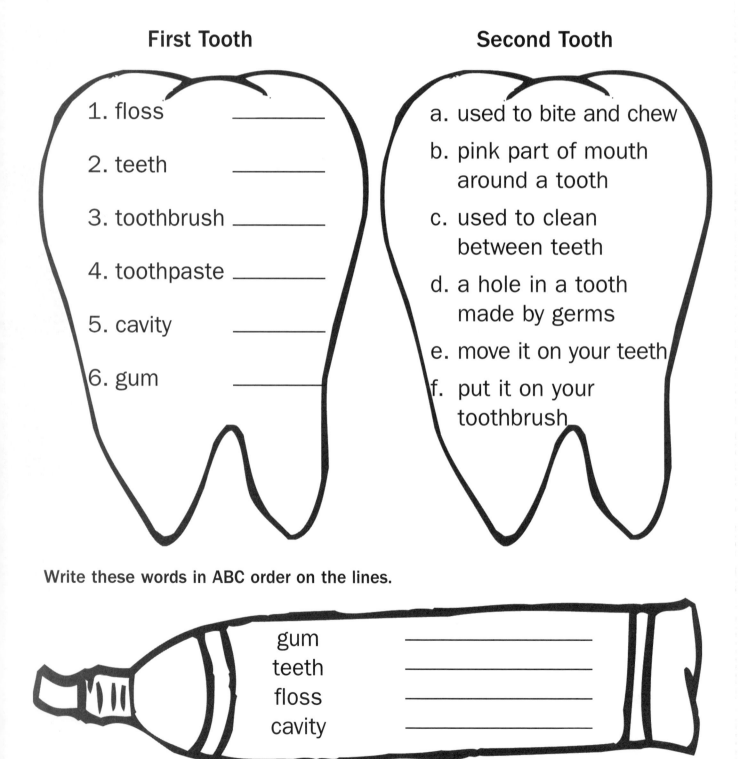

First Tooth

1. floss   _____

2. teeth   _____

3. toothbrush _____

4. toothpaste _____

5. cavity   _____

6. gum   _____

Second Tooth

a. used to bite and chew

b. pink part of mouth around a tooth

c. used to clean between teeth

d. a hole in a tooth made by germs

e. move it on your teeth

f. put it on your toothbrush

Write these words in ABC order on the lines.

gum   _____

teeth   _____

floss   _____

cavity   _____

How We Stay Safe

1

Name _____

We stay safe when we walk. Choose the best word. Write it on the line.

> **sidewalk   cross   grownup   cars   street**

1. Always walk with a _____ .

2. Walk on a path or a _____ .

3. Stop and look both ways before you cross a

_____ .

4. Always _____ a street at a corner.

5. Never walk between parked _____ .

Write the color word on the line to show what each means.

This means cars must stop.   _____

This means cars must slow   _____
down and get ready to stop.

This means cars may go.   _____

How We Stay Safe

Name _____

We stay safe on wheels.

Write the correct word or words under each picture.

bike path	wheel	helmet
skateboard	grownup	brakes

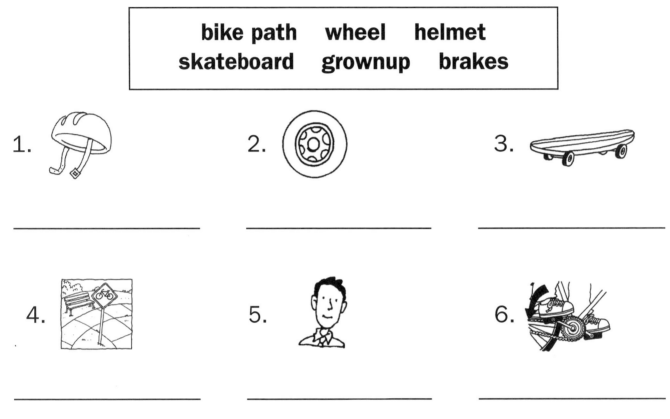

1. _____

2. _____

3. _____

4. _____

5. _____

6. _____

If it is a safety word, color the helmet.

stop   look   bike path   brakes   clown

DAILY VOCABULARY PRACTICE

How We Stay Safe

Name _____

We stay safe in the water.

Circle the word that names each picture in the sentence.

1. Always swim with a near.   mouse   grown up

2. Wear a [picture] if you cannot swim.   horse   life jacket

3. Do not [picture] into the water.   jump   sing

4. Always swim with a [picture] .   buddy   bike

5. Never swim if you see [picture] .   sun   lightning

When you are swimming

There's lots and lots of sun.

What can you wear

To stay safe and have fun?

Write the first letter of each picture name on the line to find the answer.

____ ____ ____ ____ ____ ____ ____ ____

DAILY VOCABULARY PRACTICE

Name _____

A. If a word is an Earth word color the globe.

1. land

2. beach

3. wind

4. rain

5. clown

6. earthquake

7. trees

8. seasons

9. mitten

10. air

B. Circle the correct picture answer.

1. Which is a set of bones?

2. Which is in your chest?

3. Which helps keep you healthy?

4. Which cares for your teeth?

5. Which helps keep you safe?

DAILY VOCABULARY PRACTICE

Math We Use

Name _____

We use math each day.

Draw a line to match the number to the number word.

0.   ten

1.   eight

2.   zero

3.   seven

4.   nine

5.   three

6.   four

7.   six

8.   one

9.   two

10.   five

Look at the number word and draw that many apples in each bowl.

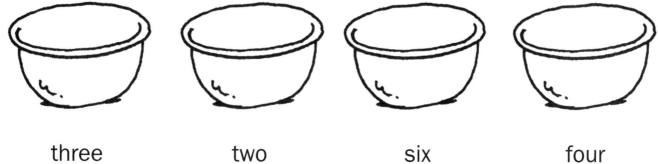

three   two   six   four

DAILY VOCABULARY PRACTICE

Math We Use

Name _____

We work with numbers. Choose the correct word and write it on the line.

> **subtract   group   add   compare   order**

1. to put two numbers together   _____

2. to take a smaller number
   from a bigger number   _____

3. to put a number of things together   _____

4. to put numbers correctly
   one after the other   _____

5. to find if a number is more
   than or less than another   _____

Read the little story. Then answer each question.

Jon wanted to **solve** a problem. He took **ten** beans. He **added** three more beans. He now had thirteen beans. He learned that thirteen beans are **more than** ten beans.

1. Which dark word means to
   put two numbers together?

   _____

2. Which dark word means to
   find an answer?

   _____

3. Which dark words mean to
   compare numbers of things?

   _____

4. Which dark word rhymes
   with hen?

   _____

Math We Use

Name _____

We use math words.

Draw a line from the word to the thing that it names.

1. order

2. number word

3. pattern $3 + 2 = 5$

4. number sentence eight

5. set 1, ____, 3, 4, ____, 6

Color the boxes to make your own pattern.

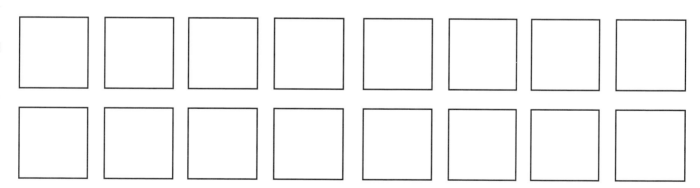

The Shapes of Things

1

Name _____

Write the name of the shape on the line.

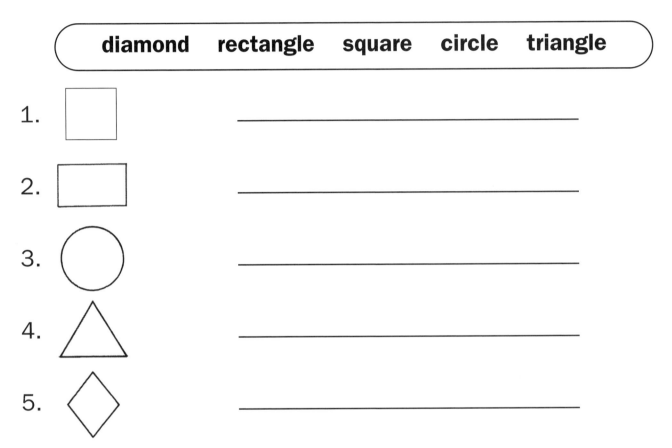

diamond   rectangle   square   circle   triangle

1. _____

2. _____

3. _____

4. _____

5. _____

Use any of the shapes above to make a picture. Use as many as you need.

DAILY VOCABULARY PRACTICE

The Shapes of Things

Name _____

Write a word from the Word Bank on the line.

| sides   pizza   baseball   big   box |

1. "We will send it in a square _____,"said mother.

2. "Let's go outside and make a _____ circle," said the teacher.

3. My piece of _____ looks like a triangle.

4. The players love that _____ diamond.

5. Our yard is a rectangle with four straight _____.

Write the name of each shape under the picture.

| rectangle   triangle   circle |

_____ _____ _____

The Shapes of Things

3

Name _____

Choose a word to finish each group of words.

rectangle   square   triangle   diamond   circle

1. I am round like a pizza. I am a _____ .

2. I am shaped like a baseball card. I am a _____ .

3. I am shaped like a piece of pie. I am a _____ .

4. My four sides are just the same. My four corners are too.

   I am a _____ .

5. I am shaped like some kites. I am a _____ .

Read each word. Write it under "Shape Words" or "Not Shape Words."

together   triangle   rope   circle

Shape Words   Not Shape Words

_____   _____

_____   _____

Graphs and Charts

Name _____

The class voted for favorite dogs. Look at the graph. Write the answer on the line.

Favorite Dog									
Beagle	🐕	🐕	🐕	🐕	🐕	🐕	🐕		
Golden Retriever	🐕	🐕	🐕	🐕	🐕				
Mutt	🐕	🐕	🐕						

1. This is a picture _____.

2. It is about favorite _____.

3. Which dog got the most votes? _____

4. Which dog got the fewest votes? _____

Draw a picture of your favorite kind of dog.

DAILY VOCABULARY PRACTICE

Graphs and Charts

Name _____

We use charts.

Choose the word and write it on the line.

> chart   most   count   snack   vote

1. Our class will vote for a favorite _____.

2. We will show our votes on a _____.

3. A tally mark will stand for one _____.

4. We will _____ the tally marks for each food on the chart.

5. The one with the _____ marks is the winner.

Foods	Number of Students							
Apples								
Carrots								
Bananas								
Celery								

3

Graphs and Charts

Name _____

Write the name of each part on the line.

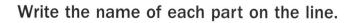

| title | key | bar graph | bar |

This is a _____ . _____

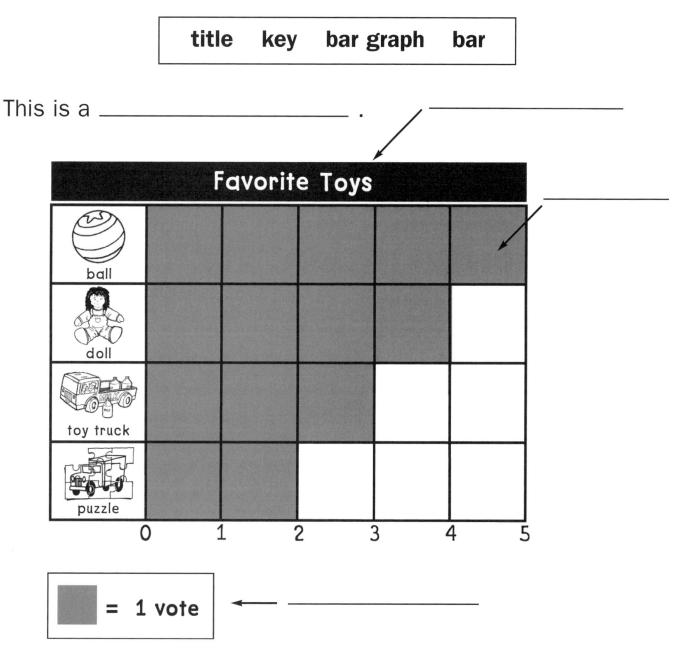

_____

Favorite Toys

ball
doll
toy truck
puzzle

0   1   2   3   4   5

▨ = 1 vote ← _____

Answer the questions.

1. Which toy got the most votes ? _____

2. Which toy got the fewest votes? _____

Calendars and Clocks

Name _____

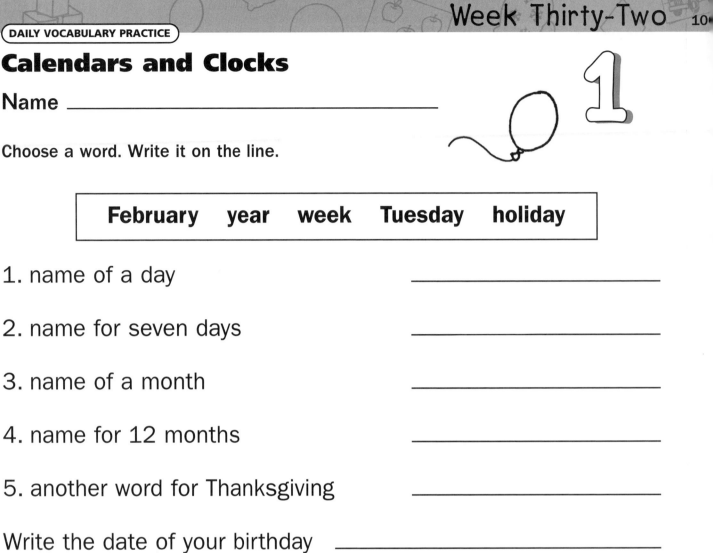

Choose a word. Write it on the line.

| February   year   week   Tuesday   holiday |

1. name of a day   _____

2. name for seven days   _____

3. name of a month   _____

4. name for 12 months   _____

5. another word for Thanksgiving   _____

Write the date of your birthday   _____

Draw a picture of what you want to do for your next birthday.

DAILY VOCABULARY PRACTICE

Calendars and Clocks

2

Name _____

Look at Jane's calendar.

November

Sunday	Monday	Tuesday	Wednesday	Thursday	Friday	Saturday
				1	2	3
4	5	6	7 flute lesson	8	9	10 School Fair
11	12	13	14 flute lesson	15	16 School Play	17
18	19	20	21 flute lesson	22 Thanksgiving	23	24
25	26	27 Dad's Birthday	28 flute lesson	29	30	

Answer each question.

1. Jane's calendar is for which month? _____

2. On which day is Dad's birthday?   _____

3. On which day is the School Fair?   _____

4. What is the date of the School Play?_____

5. Which day and date is a holiday?   _____

Try Some More!

Write each answer on the line.

1. How many Wednesdays are in this month? _____

2. Where does Jane go on Wednesdays? _____

Calendars and Clocks

Name _____

Choose a word and write it on the line.

> dentist   hops   checks   teeth   soccer

1. Jill is going to the _____ in one hour.

2. It will take about 30 minutes to clean her _____ .

3. The dentist _____ her teeth for 10 minutes.

4. Jill _____ out of the chair in five seconds.

5. Jill has only 15 minutes to get to _____ practice.

Answer each question. Follow the directions.

1. The big hand is on _____ . Color it dark blue.

2. The little hand is on _____ . Color it green.

3. Color the face of the clock light blue.

4. What time does the clock show? _____ o'clock.

DAILY VOCABULARY PRACTICE

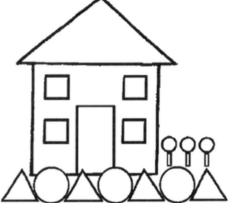

Name _____

A. Read the word. Draw a line to the correct meaning.

1. to put two numbers together   group

2. to take a smaller number   compare
   from a larger number

3. to write a group of numbers   subtract
   one after the other

4. to see if one number is   add
   larger than another

5. to put things together   order

B. Look at the drawing.
   How many shapes do you see?

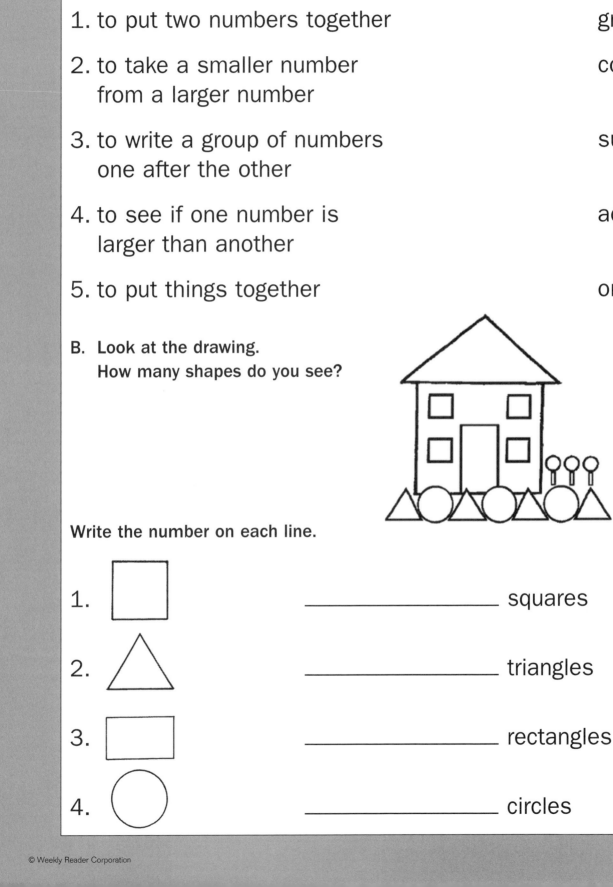

Write the number on each line.

1. _____ squares

2. _____ triangles

3. _____ rectangles

4. _____ circles

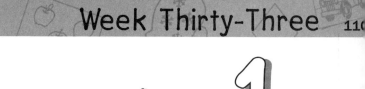

Pet Animals

Name _____

Read the words. Write them in the correct place.

elephant cat goldfish giraffe dog zebra bunny coyote

Pets	Not Pets
_____	_____
_____	_____
_____	_____
_____	_____

Choose a pet you would like to have. Then draw a special house for it to live in.

DAILY VOCABULARY PRACTICE

Pet Animals

Name _____

2

Circle the word that does not belong.

1. cat   bunny   coyote

2. dog   bee   goldfish

3. gerbil   puppy   bald eagle

4. tiger   rabbit   hamster

5. elephant   kitten   parrot

Use the words to make some silly sentences.
Add some words of your own words too.

sat   elephant   hat   mat

_____

_____

money   bunny   funny   honey

_____

_____

Pet Animals

3

Name _____

Read the rhyme. Then answer each question below.

Cat wanted some milk.

But Dog said "No,

Have some of my bone

It will help you grow."

Cat talked to the mouse

She even said "Please."

So that little mouse

Gave cat some fine cheese!

1. Which animals in the poem would be good pets?

_____ and _____

2. Which words rhyme in the poem?

_____ and _____

_____ and _____

3. Which word rhymes with silk? _____

4. Which word means the same as small? _____

DAILY VOCABULARY PRACTICE

Rain Forest Animals

Name _____

Rain forest animals fly, jump, hop, and hang.

Draw a line from the words to the matching rain forest animal.

1. it flies with light wings

2. it jumps in trees and howls

3. it hops on the ground

4. it hops on branches and eats with a big bill

5. it hangs and does not move

Get the frog to the bug!

Rain Forest Animals

Name _____

Circle the correct picture answer.

1. Which is a rain forest cat?

2. Which is a rain forest bird?

3. Which is a rain forest mammal

How many words can you make using the letters in *rain forest*?

Write them on the lines.

_____

_____

_____

_____

_____

Rain Forest Animals

Name _____

Many animal groups are found in the rain forest.

Choose which animal group each one belongs to.
Write it on the line.

> **snake   monkey   insect   cat   lizard**

1. iguana   _____

2. jaguar   _____

3. beetle   _____

4. howler   _____

5. boa   _____

Farm Animals

Name _____

Some farm animals lay eggs.

Draw a line from the picture to the word.

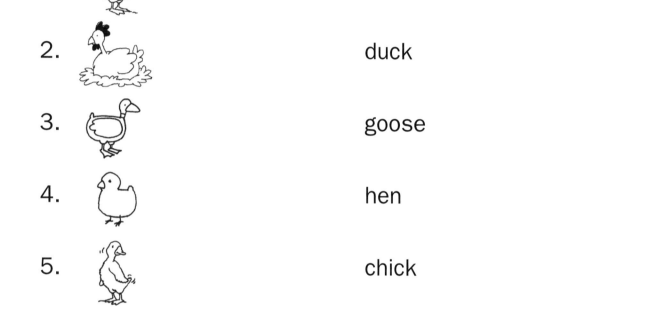

1.   duckling

2.   duck

3.   goose

4.   hen

5.   chick

Write the answer to each question on the line.

1. Which word above rhymes with *pen*? _____

2. Which word above rhymes with *moose*? _____

3. Which word above names a *baby duck*? _____

4. Write two words that rhyme with *chick*.

_____ and _____

DAILY VOCABULARY PRACTICE

Farm Animals

Name _____

Some farm animals have live babies.

Choose a word and write it in the sentence.

| calf | pig | cow | horse | goat |

1. "Oink," said the _____.

2. "Mooo," said the _____.

3. The cow has a baby _____.

4. Look at the _____ run!

5. Our _____ eats twigs.

Follow each direction.

_____ _____ _____ _____

1. The first pig is named Bessy. Write her name on the line and color her pink.

2. The last pig is named Tessy. Write her name and give her a red fuzzy coat.

3. The third pig is named Jessy. Write her name and give her green boots.

4. The second is named Messy. Write her name then color her so she matches her name.

Farm Animals

Name _____

Write each answer on the line.

1. This farm animal's name rhymes with *boat*. What is it?

    _____

2. This farm animal's name rhymes with *sleep*. What is it?

    _____

3. This farm animal's name rhymes with *half*. What is it?

    _____

4. This farm animal's name rhymes with *loose*. What is it?

    _____

5. This farm animal's name rhymes with *luck*. What is it?

    _____

Circle the word that means the same as the underlined word.

1. Cara calf is a happy calf.

    glad   sad

2. She calls to all her friends.

    turns   yells

3. Cara likes her special place in the sun.

    lost   spot

4. She starts each day there.

    begins   long

Water Animals

Name _____

Some water animals have live babies.

Draw a line from the picture to the word.

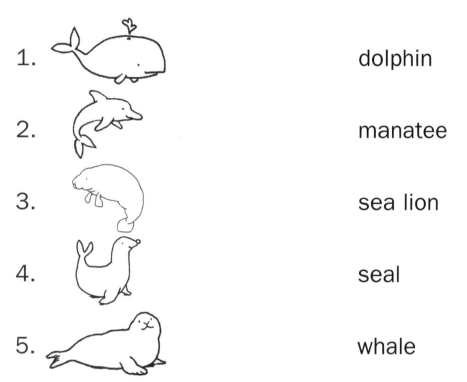

1.   dolphin

2.   manatee

3.   sea lion

4.   seal

5.   whale

Get the baby seal to his mother. Follow the path that has only water words.

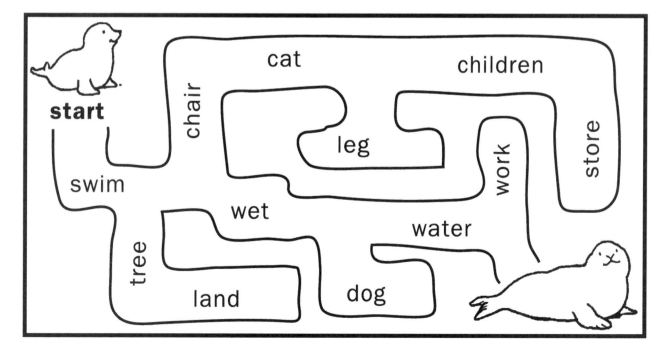

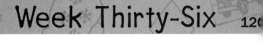

Water Animals

Name _____

Some water animals lay eggs.

Look at the picture and draw a line to the animal name.

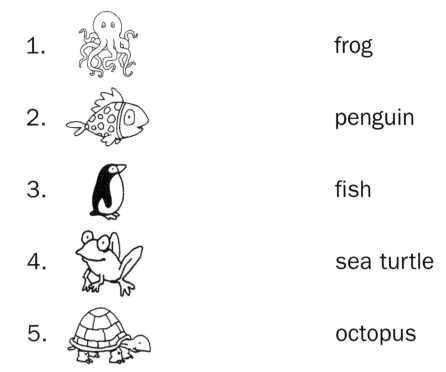

1.   frog

2.   penguin

3.   fish

4.   sea turtle

5.   octopus

Find fish, frog, penguin, and octopus in the puzzle. Go across or down.

```
O X O F X O F
X O X R O X I
O C T O P U S
X X O G X O H
P E N G U I N
```

Water Animals

Name _____

Some water animals have different shapes.

Draw a line from the picture to the name of each animal.

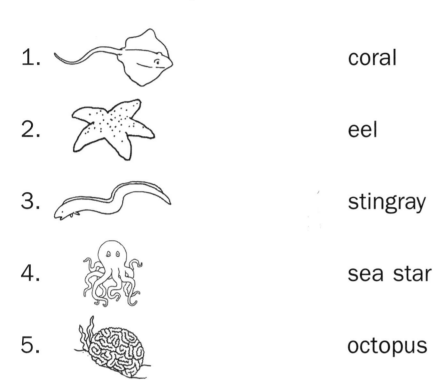

1.   coral

2.   eel

3.   stingray

4.   sea star

5.   octopus

1. Flat and wide, I like to hide.

   I am a _____.

2. I'm an animal, but I look like a block of rock.

   I am a _____.

3. I have five arms but do no harm.

   I am a _____.

4. People are charmed with my eight arms.

   I am an _____.

5. I look a bit like a snake, but that's not me, make no mistake.

   I am an _____.

DAILY VOCABULARY PRACTICE

Name _____

A. Circle the name of the animal that would be a house pet.

1. tiger   kitten   leopard

2. goat   goldfish   elephant

3. bear   puppy   coyote

4. hamster   lion   giraffe

5. cow   camel   cat

B. Circle the correct picture answer.

1. Which says "Moo?"

2. Which lays eggs?

3. Which has live babies?

4. Which baby is a foal?

5. Which one's name rhymes with beep?

6. Which one has a calf?

Daily Vocabulary Practice
Answers — Grade 1

Week One

Day One: 1. two/2 dots, 2 fly/bird, 3. run/boys running, 4. one/one dot, 5. sad/sad face

Day Two: Check students' answers.

Day Three: 1. ask, 2. She, 3. now, 4. eat, 5. are

two, a number; new, not old; out, not in; her, not him.

Week Two

Day One: Dog—play, runs, eats, good

Day Two: 1. down the slide, 2. at my house, 3. ride a horse, 4. come to me, 5. open the door

Review students' pictures.

Day Three: 1.-5. ride, play, find, sing, jump

give/present, ride/horse

Week Three

Day One: 1.warm, 2. help, 3. make, 4. went, 5. blue

Check students' stars.

Day Two: over, down, under, there

Check students' drawings.

Day Three: 1. jump, 2. walk, 3. sing, 4. give, 5. ride

1. elephant, 2. girl, 3. dog, 4. frog

Week Four

Day One: Color Words: yellow, blue, brown, green; Not Color Words: going, under, there

Review students' drawings.

Day Two: 1. little, 2. under, 3. down, 4. take, 5. white

Day Three: 1. clown, 2. jacket, 3. 4 stars, 4. ball, 5. child

1. child, 2. pizza, 3. horse

Month 1 Review

A. 1. She is up. 2. It is his. 3. It is warm. 4. It can jump. 5. It is pretty.

B.

C. 1. duck, monkey, 2. toy chest, 3. pizza, moon, 4. mitten, scarf

Week Five

Day One: 1. man/fan, 2. big/pig, 3. red/bed, 4. pick/sick, 5. jay/day

My/sky

Day Two: Check students' words. Possible words: van, can, man, pan, fan

Check students' pictures.

Day Three: 1. cat, 2. bat, 3. rat, 4. hat, 5. mat

Review students' sentences.

Week Six

Day One: 1. yes, 2. yes, 3. no, 4. yes, 5. yes, 6. no, 7. yes, 8. yes, 9. yes, 10. no; bee, lion, us, eat, blue

Day Two: 1. go, 2. own, 3. nose, 4. open, 5. hold;

Review students' sentences.

Day Three: 1.nice, 2. bike, 3. Hide, 4. line, 5. tire;

smile, light, bite, kite

Week Seven

Day One: 1.fat, 2. lap, 3. ran, 4. hat, 5. bat;

1. hat, 2. map, 3. pad, 4. tan

Day Two: 1. big, 2. kitten, 3.wish, 4. pet, 5. wet

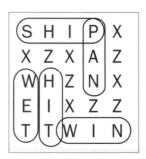

Day Three: 1. hops, 2. cut, 3. Mom, 4. mop, 5.duck; Check students' pictures.

Week Eight

Day One: 1. need, 2. food, 3. sleep, 4. seed, 5. school; Check students' matching.

Day Two: Living: bee, sheep, tree, weed; Nonliving book, cheese, floor, room; Check students' pictures.

Day Three: 1. green, 2. tooth, 3. cook, 4. food, 5. see

1. spoon, 2. tooth, 3. door, 4. foot

Month 2 Review

A. 1. meet/street, 2. run/sun, 3. side/wide, 4. bark/park, 5. boat/float

B. 1. bed, 2. hen,

Week Nine

Day One: Check students' matching.

Correct maze path: boy, mother, girl, father, grandma

Day Two: Place: park, zoo, home, school; Not a Place: bike, box, dog, ant

Check students' drawings.

Day Three: 1. glass, 2. bed, 3. food, 4. kite, 5. boat

Week Ten

Day One: 1. bank, 2. hospital, 3. restaurant, 4. Strong School, 5. garage

Check students' drawings.

Day Two: 1. Tom Jones, 2. Mr. Platt, 3. Sara Bert, 4. Mrs. Harris, 5. Jon Ross

1. Jane Moody, 2. Dr. Fred Ryan, 3. Long Lane School

Day Three: 1. Mrs. Miller, 2. Apple Hill School, 3. Principal White, 4. Jon Miller, 5.Royal Candy Factory

Week Eleven

Day One: Move: run, hop, walk, swim;Don't Move: paper, very, king, toy

Check students' drawings.

Day Two: 1. think, 2. miss, 3. hope, 4. wants, 5. knows

1. A, 2. C, 3. B

Day Three: 1. child, 2. rabbit, 3. man, 4. mother, 5. chef

Check students' drawings

Week Twelve

Day One: 1. black ants, 2. red apple, 3. green grass, 4. white snow, 5. yellow sun

Check students' drawings.

Day Two: Review students' drawings and sentences.

Day Three: 1. mean/ grumpy man, 2. silly/dog, 3. pretty/ girl with flower, 4. sad/ clown face, 5. noisy/train on tracks; song

Month 3 Review

A. 1. yellow, 2. yellow, 3. yellow, 4. green, 5. green, 6. red, 7. red, 8. yellow, 9. red, 10. green,

B. 1. school, 2. dad, 3. apple, 4. zoo, 5. bike

Week Thirteen

Day One: 1. I, 2. We, 3. You, 4. They, 5. She

1. girls and boy, 2. 1 boy, 3. 1 girl, 4. woman

Day Two: 1. them, 2. me, 3. their, 4. his, 5. us

1. test/best, kid/did, 2. the teacher, 3. baby goats

Day Three: 1. hers, 2. yours, 3. their, 4. our, 5. her

1. his, 2. theirs, 3. hers, 4. ours

Week Fourteen

Day One: 1. grandmother, 2. grandfather, 3. airplane, 4. breakfast, 5. birthday; Check students' matching.

1. cupcake, 2. doghouse,
3. blackbird

Day Two: 1. baseball,
2. fireplace, 3. playground,
4. snowflake, 5. starfish

1. first star red, 2. yellow
star /eyes and smile,
3. Responses will vary.

Day Three: 1. someone,
2. without, 3. outside,
4. everywhere, 5. maybe

1. pancake, 2. birthday,
3. homework, 4. outside,
5. pancake and birthday
fish are going to the right

Week Fifteen

Day One: 1. ant/bug,
2. small/little, 3. house/
home, 4. nice/kind,
5. woman/lady

Color: dinner

Day Two: 1. bee, 2. harm,
3. shout, 4. store, 5. hop;

leave/go, hello/hi,
house/home, loud/noisy,
shout/yell

Day Three: 1. yellow,
2. yellow, 3. red, 4. yellow,
5. yellow, yellow

kind: nice, sweet, caring,
thoughtful

Week Sixteen

Day One: 1. arrow
down/arrow up, 2. gate
open/door closed,
3. happy face/sad face,
4. in doghouse/outside
doghouse, 5. top of
slide/bottom of stairs

Review students' drawings.

Day Two: 1. happy, 2. big,
3. stop, 4. day, 5. cold

big/little, go/come,
over/under, low/high

Day Three: 1. up, 2. open,
3. runs, 4. new, 5. always

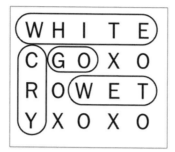

Month 4 Review

A. 1. Change we to us,
2. change is to it,
3. change my to me

B. 1. up/down, 2. over/
under, 3. back/front,
4. start/stop, 5. in/out,

C. 1. butterfly/insect,
2. backpack, a bag,
3. bedroom/place to sleep

Week Seventeen

Day One: Review students'
matches and pictures.

Day Two: 1. jet/large fast
plane, 2. fly/move through
air, 3. airplane/plane with
wings,

4. runway/place for planes;

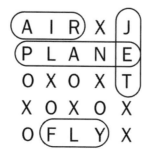

Day Three: 1. c, 2. e, 3. d,
4. b, 5. a; Correct order:
3, 4, 2, 1.

Week Eighteen

Day One: Color: 2, 4, 5, 6;
Check students' drawings.

Day Two: Check students'
matches. Check students'
drawings.

Day Three: 1. mix, 2. bake,
3. boil, 4. fry, 5. stove

1. shake and make, 2. in
and grin, 3. mix, 4. spoon

Week Nineteen

Day One: Check students'
matches. Rhyming word:
socks

Day Two: 1. coat,
2. mittens, 3. scarf, 4. hat,
5. boots; 1. boots,
2. mittens, 3. hat

Day Three: 1. swim suit,
2. shorts, 3. sandals,
4. swim suit,
5. sunglasses;

1. sun, 2. hat. 3. shorts

Week Twenty

Day One: 1. house of dry
mud, 2. home for a king,
3. one-story house, 4. a
building with many homes,
5. can have wheels and
move around

Review students' drawings.

Day Two: 1. nest,
2. burrow, 3. hive, 4. dog
house, 5. barn

Review children's drawings.

Day Three: Check students' matches. Check students' drawings.

Month 5 Review

A. Yes: car, boat, jet, ship, road, wagon

No: happy, sing, sleep, those, pan, nice

B. Milk: cheese, yogurt; Fruits: blueberry, orange; Vegetables: carrot, corn;

Week Twenty–One

Day One: 1. up, 2. hot, 3. all, 4. grow, 5. went

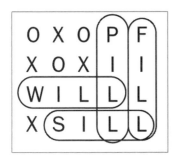

Day Two: Water: river, ocean, pond, lake; Not Water: street, walk, hop, clown

Check students' drawings.

Day Three: 1. take, 2. go, 3. near, 4. us, 5. shows, 6. that

1. globe, 2. directions, 3. map key, 4. state

Week Twenty–Two

Day One: 1. Valentine's Day, 2. Halloween, 3. Thanksgiving, 4. Presidents' Day, 5. Christmas; Check students' drawings.

Day Two: Let's Celebrate: sing, laugh, dance, talk, games, eat;

Color: cake, piñata, Valentine

Day Three: 1. Valentine's Day, 2. card, 3. cupcakes, 4. time, 5. all

Check students' sentences.

Week Twenty–Three

Day One: 1.leader of country, 2. president's home, 3. Washington, D.C., 4. United States, 5. stars and stripes

Check students' flags.

Day Two: 1. help, 2. fair, 3. trust, 4. cares, 5. count on

Check students' matches.

Day Three: Correct sentence: Our president is a leader.

Week Twenty–Four

Day One: 1. leads, 2. lunch, 3. papers, 4. books, 5. special

Possible rhyming words: bunch, munch, crunch

Day Two: Place: town, store, playground, People: family, neighbors, friends, Thing: car, table, TV

Check students' drawings.

Day Three: 1. baker, 2. firefighter, 3. police officer, 4. traffic guard, 5. doctor, 6. dentist, 7. mail carrier, 8. nurse;

1. stay, 2. school, 3. traffic

Month 6 Review

A. 1. map, 2. lake. 3. ball, 4. island, 5. mountain, 6. ocean, 7. road, 8. state

B. 1. red 2. purple, 3. red, 4. purple, 5. red, 6. red, 7. purple, 8. red, 9. purple, 10. purple

Week Twenty–Five

Day One: 1. land, 2. cave, 3. air, 4. rain, 5. beach, 6. water

Checks students' work.

Day Two: 1. fall, 2. trees, 3. sky, 4. blow, 5. shakes, 6. harm;

Rhyming Words: answers will vary.

Day Three: 1. Turn , 2. Keep, 3. litter, 4. cans, 5. clean;

1. park, 2. rock, 3. save

Week Twenty–Six

Day One: 1. planet, 2. moon, 3. sun, 4. stars, 5. solar system

Tic Tac Toe: sun, planet, moon

Day Two: Check students labels and coloring.

Day Three: 1. astronaut, 2. space station, 3. space shuttle, 4. blast off! 5. orbit;

Answer: Neptune

Week Twenty–Seven

Day One: 1. skeleton, 2. feet, 3. heart, 4. brain, 5. lungs.

1. yes, 2. yes, 3. no

Day Two: 1. nurse, 2. sick, 3. X ray, 4. medicine, 5. well

Message: Get a checkup every year.

Day Three: 1. c, 2. a, 3. e, 4. f, 5. d, 6. b

ABC order: cavity, floss, gum, teeth

Week Twenty–Eight

Day One: 1. grown-up, 2. sidewalk, 3. street, 4. cross, 5. cars

Color Words: red, yellow, green

Day Two: 1. helmet, 2. wheel, 3. skateboard, 4. bike path, 5. grown-up, 6. brakes

Colored helmets: stop, look, bike path, brakes

Day Three: 1. grown-up, 2. life jacket, 3. jump, 4. buddy, 5. lightning;

Answer: sunscreen

Month 7 Review

A. Color: land, beach, wind, rain, earthquake, trees, seasons, air

B. 1. skeleton, 2. heart, 3. exercise, 4. dentist, 5. helmet

Week Twenty–Nine

Day One: Number Words: zero, one, two, three, four, five, six, seven, eight, nine, ten

Check students' drawings.

Day Two: 1. add, 2. subtract, 3. group, 4. order, 5. compare;

1. added, 2. solve, 3. more than, 4. ten

Day Three: 1. 1,___3, 4, ___6, 2. eight, 3. mitten pattern, 4. 3 + 2 = 5, 5. 3 apples in a box

1. Check students' patterns.

Week Thirty

Day One: 1. square, 2. rectangle, 3. circle, 4. triangle, 5. diamond; Review students pictures.

Day Two: 1. box, 2. big, 3. pizza, 4. baseball, 5. sides;

pizza: circle, juice box: rectangle, pie: triangle

Day Three: 1.circle, 2. rectangle, 3. triangle, 4. square, 5. diamond;

1. Shape Words: triangle, circle; Not: rope, together

Week Thirty-One

Day One: 1. graph, 2. dogs, 3. beagle, 4. mutt

Day Two: 1. snack, 2. chart, 3. vote, 4. count, 5. most

Review students' charts.

Day Three: Check students' labels.

1. ball, 2. puzzle

Week Thirty-Two

Day One: 1. Tuesday, 2. week, 3. February, 4. year, 5. holiday;

Check students' birthdates and pictures.

Day Two: 1. November, 2. Tuesday, 3. Saturday, 4. Friday, November 16, 5. Thursday, November 22;

Try Some More: 1. four, 2. Flute lessons

Day Three: 1. dentist, 2. teeth, 3. checks, 4. hops, 5. soccer;

1. 12, 2. 7, 3. & 4 Check tracing and coloring, 5. 7

Month 8 Review

A. 1. add, 2. subtract, 3. order, 4. compare, 5. group

B. 1. 5 squares, 2. 5 triangles, 3. 4 rectangles, 4. 6 circles

Week Thirty-Three

Day One: Pets: bunny, cat, dog, goldfish; Not Pets: coyote, elephant, giraffe, zebra;

Check students' drawings.

Day Two: 1. coyote, 2. bee, 3. bald eagle, 4. tiger, 5. elephant;

Review students' sentences.

Day Three: 1. cat and dog, 2. No and grow, please and cheese, 3. milk, 4. little

Week Thirty-Four

Day One: 1. butterfly, 2. howler monkey, 3. frog, 4. toucan, 5. sloth;

Day Two: 1. ocelot, 2. toucan, 3. sloth

Review students' words.

Day Three: 1. lizard, 2. cat, 3. insect, 4. monkey, 5. snake;

Week Thirty-Five

Day One: Check students' matches.

1. hen, 2. goose, 3. duckling, 4. Answers will vary.

Day Two: 1. pig, 2. cow, 3. calf, 4. horse 5. goat;

Check students' drawings.

Day Three: 1. goat, 2. sheep, 3. calf, 4. goose, 5. duck;

1. glad, 2. yells, 3. spot, 4. begins

Week Thirty-Six

Day One: Review students' matches.

Correct path words: swim, wet, water

Day Two: Check students' matches.

```
O X O F X O F
X O X R O X I
O C T O P U S
X X O G X O H
P E N G U I N
```

Day Three: 1. stingray, 2. sea star, 3. eel, 4. octopus, 5. coral;

1. stingray, 2. coral, 3. sea star, 4. octopus, 5. eel

Month 9 Review

A. 1. kitten, 2. goldfish, 3. puppy, 4. hamster, 5. cat

B. 1. cow, 2. hen, 3. goat, 4. young horse, 5. sheep, 6. cow